Penguin Books
The Village Cricket Match

John Parker has been an enthusiastic cricketer from the age of twelve when he first appeared for Danbury in Essex against Tolleshunt d'Arcy. He was captain of the City of London School Cricket XI, received tuition in wicket-keeping from Tommy Wade of Essex fame and more recently made a hundred before lunch for Independent Television News against the BBC.

He worked on the *Essex Chronicle*, the *Midlands Daily Tribune* and from 1955 to 1966 was a member of the Press Association in Rhodesia, where he was President of the Rhodesian Guild of Journalists. John Parker was the first journalist to be expelled from Rhodesia and since 1966 he has worked for ITN as writer, reporter and foreign editor, and is currently Sports Editor.

John Parker's previous publications are *Rhodesia: Little White Island* (1973) and *Great Art Sales of the Century* (1975).

John Parker

The Village Cricket Match

Penguin Books

Penguin Books Ltd, Harmondsworth,
Middlesex, England
Penguin Books, 625 Madison Avenue,
New York, New York 10022, U.S.A.
Penguin Books Australia Ltd, Ringwood,
Victoria, Australia
Penguin Books Canada Ltd, 2801 John Street
Markham, Ontario, Canada L3R 1B4
Penguin Books (N.Z.) Ltd, 182–190 Wairau Road,
Auckland 10, New Zealand

First published by Weidenfeld and Nicolson 1977
Published in Penguin Books 1978

Made and printed in Great Britain by
Cox & Wyman Ltd, London, Reading and Fakenham
Set in Linotype Juliana

The author wishes to apologize to:

the ghost of Hugh de Selincourt, for presuming to replay his 'Cricket Match' some fifty or so years later; sundry great cricketers, past and present, whose names flit occasionally into these pages and out again, merely for verisimilitude; and all those who may think they recognize themselves or their friends in this book. They are mistaken, as all the characters are creatures of my imagination. If you have met one of them at any time, it must have been on a cricket pitch.

Chapter 1

Tillingfold still lies under the lee of the South Downs, just as it did fifty years ago, and eight hundred or more before that, according to the Parish Records. Some older residents, particularly those who belong to the South Downs Archaeological Society, insist that there was a Roman settlement here, and an important one too; and they point for proof to the well-preserved ruins of the villa of Catullus Quintus Minimus, two miles away and facing the warm south, which were excavated by Sir Mortimer Wheeler only a few years ago. Well, between the wars, anyway.

Certainly the line of the hills hasn't changed, frowning grey in the winter but protecting Tillingfold from the south-westerly gales that sweep up the English Channel from October to March. In spring and in summer, especially in a memorable one such as this, they acquire a presence that can be found nowhere else in the world. In the early July morning, when the number of villagers out and about can be counted on the fingers of one hand, the Downs are decked with a thin white mist, rising from the chimney-pots and television aerials of Tillingfold to a line just beneath the crown of the hills. Now is the time to fly over Sussex, with the rising sun ricocheting off the hill-tops, the villages still asleep in the shadows under their filmy coverlets, and to the south, the bold sweep down to the tangle of housing estates, motorways, oil tanks and electricity grids, which lines the south coast in the name of progress.

Better still, thought Gauvinier, to be good and alive and on your own two feet, climbing through the thinning mist at six o'clock on a morning of high summer. There was something in climbing like this, solitary exercise for its own sake, that was cleansing, invigorating, even purifying. Gauvinier grinned as his mind gave birth to the conceit. He could taste the whisky at the back of his throat and the nicotine in his nose. Purifying? He needed something to clear his lungs and his brain after the long session in the back parlour of 'The Red Lion' last night, when they'd thrashed out the side for the most important match of the year – the annual gala match against Raveley.

Breathing deeply, Gauvinier broke through the last remnants of the mist and stepped out on to the broad breast of the down. As he did so, the sun seemed to leap out at him, warming him suddenly through and through. He squinted against the glare and turned, looking back across the valley and down to the village. Half a mile away and two hundred feet below him Tillingfold lay stretched out like a relief map for his inspection. He realized the sun had taken less than five minutes to clear the mist.

Not for the first time, he reflected that Tillingfold wasn't a picturesque village. It had been spared the squalor of the seafront development by the bulk of the Downs. The long arm of the motorways had not reached it. It was connected with outer civilization by what the Roads Department and the Automobile Association termed an 'A' road but was more than five miles off the north–south trunks which formed the arteries between London and the coast. The weekend tripper had to work quite hard to drive through Tillingfold, which indeed had little enough (apart from the Roman villa, and that could be 'done' in twenty minutes) to offer him.

The High Street lay roughly east–west. Its one hundred and fifty or so yards of nondescript shops and offices broadened out in the centre into a very small square, flagstoned off the road's tarmac and now used as a car park. Off the square the road s-bent itself sharply and narrowly between four genuine Queen Anne houses. The best kept of the four, repointed and touched in cream and lime green, showed the name of a famous London firm of estate agents; properties discreetly displayed in its bow windows ranged from the £120,000 'period farmhouse and grounds, suitable for development', to the whitewashed and thatched cottage on Tillingfold Hill, labelled 'only £20,000 two-bedroomed thatched country cottage, suitable holiday home for young romantic couple'. Gauvinier, strolling by the previous evening on his way to the cricket club selection meeting, had stared. Twenty thousand pounds . . . he himself could remember the labourers' cottages on the hillside, with one tap and one bucket 'privy' between them, falling empty and into disrepair as agricultural wages and conditions had boomed during the war and its aftermath. Young Fred Bason, the builder's son (not so young now, thought Gauvinier, as he recalled his own age) had bought them in the early fifties, four of them for £1000, each with their little gardens front and behind. He'd boarded up the doors and windows and left them to time and two generations of Tillingfold children, while he wrestled with his father's business.

Many a time he'd said to Gauvinier in his slow Sussex way: 'Just you wait and see. They'll come to summat in the end.' And after he'd landed his first major contract to build the housing estate on the far side of the village he'd applied for planning permission to modernize the cottages. Now they were spick, and white, and half-timbered, with oil-fired central heating, bathrooms and brand new thatch. And £20,000 each.

So Tillingfold had grown and developed, jogging along twenty years or so behind the rest of the twentieth century. 'The Red Lion', an old coach-house, had been taken over by the brewers and 'renovated' into a mixture of Victorian Gothic, plush purple stools, horse-brasses and copper knick-knacks. But, thought Gauvinier, contemplating its roof of foot-square Horsham tiles, at least they'd spared the exterior.

Past 'The Red Lion' to the left, the High Street straightened itself out and widened slightly, skirting 'The Dog and Duck' with its bricked-in car park ('Coaches and Children Welcome; Garden at Rear'); and then it ran on past the coast road turn-off and a clutter of garages, along down the gentle slope to the village pond on the one side and the cricket field on the other.

At its best, which was usually in late spring, the pond sported two or three brace of ducks, a moorhen or two, and a smart fringe of water-lilies, as well as an abundance of water. At its worst, which to Gauvinier was the rest of the year, its natural spring dried out and it presented itself to the onlooker as caked mud, green slime and an assortment of bottles and rusting Coca-Cola cans. From time to time the Parish Council had tried to make something of the pond, but over the past forty years Gauvinier could recall only a single major effort, when the whole thing was scoured clean and the sides bricked up. One never-to-be-forgotten year a pair of swans took up residence in the rushes, on the far side from the road: another summer two Canada Geese flew in from the snows of the Arctic and stayed a month or two. But such exotic visitors soon departed, frightened away by catapults or by the smell of old oil from Sam Stacey's garage.

As the battlefield where so many hopes had been realized, illusions shattered and memorable contests staged, Tillingfold cricket field had a singularly uninspiring appearance. Gauvinier, looking down from the hill as the morning sun strengthened, wondered as he had done a thousand times before what it was that made cricket, and Tillingfold cricket in particular, of such importance, not only to him but to so many others in the village – whether they played the game or not. The cricket field was in reality the village recreation ground, with swings for the children in one corner and a wood-and-iron roundabout. Surprisingly, it had never yet killed anyone. In another corner, a simple granite cross was fenced off by spiked iron railings; this was the memorial to the dead of the village in two wars, 1914–18 names on the left, 1939–45 on the right. The curious who took the trouble to count the names discovered that forty-nine were listed as having died in the First World War, thirty-six in the Second, and that nineteen of those names occurred in each list. Further investigation in the Parish Records or in the County Archives in Chichester would uncover some of the same names among the redcoats who fought with Wellington in Spain; twelve more of them in the party from Tillingfold which lit the beacons on the Downs to warn of the Armada's coming; and another six on the roll of those who stormed Agincourt with Harry.

Some of this possibly explained Gauvinier's feelings that Wednesday morning in mid-July, even though his father's name, Paul, was inscribed in the stone of the right-hand face of the memorial by the cricket field. Although he had been born in Tillingfold and lived nearly all his forty-seven years there, he still felt only with the village, and not a part of it. He had inherited three things from his father: a whimsical nature given to flashes of inspiration and melancholy; a sense of the ridiculous that had often brought him to grief, while at the same time making him one of the more sought-after advertising copy-writers in London; and a deep overriding passion for the game of cricket.

Paul Gauvinier had married late and died too early – at Dunkirk. His son Peter had been born at the County Hospital, while Paul was making his highest score as Tillingfold's captain (eighty-eight) and winning the match against Billington during the Great Depression. Peter's mother had had to wait until after nine o'clock in the evening before her husband, triumphant, flushed, smelling of bitter and very apologetic, arrived to salute the birth of his only child. The village said that until her death she never forgave him, which, like much of Tillingfold gossip, had enough of the truth in it to be malicious. Certainly she used to refer to her marriage deprecatingly: 'I married a man with a mistress – cricket,' she would say, and her friends would smile and nod in agreement.

One of Peter Gauvinier's earliest memories was of watching his father plant one of the row of thirty chestnut trees that now lined the road side of the cricket field. Peter had been three years old, and the proud possessor of a brand new tricycle. Later that day, with the gala match in progress, he'd been pedalling figures-of-eight round the saplings on the boundary when he was startled by a great shout. Something struck him smartly on the side of the head and he was knocked head-over-heels off the tricycle on to the grass. There was the sound of screaming (his mother) and he noticed a shiny red cricket ball on the ground beside him. He picked it up and held it out to his father who, running desperately from the crease, had outstripped the field to his son and was lifting him anxiously, feeling him all over for fatal injuries. Finding none, he gave him a spanking kiss, tossed the ball to a Raveley fielder, and trotted back to the crease. 'That'll teach you to watch the ball when you're on a cricket field,' he called, halfway back, and Peter felt in his child's heart a glow of pure delight on being spoken to like a man. Then his head began to hurt, and in spite of his new manhood, he allowed the tears to trickle so that he could feel the different satisfaction of being comforted at his mother's soft breast while she muttered, over and over again, 'He might have killed his own son. He might have killed his own son.'

Strangely, Peter recalled another moment some years later, when he was eight. Tillingfold were in the field and one of the opposing batsmen stepped out and hit the ball almost straight up towards the heavens. Peter crammed his small knuckles in his mouth to stop himself yelling at the top of his voice, 'Go on, Dad,' as he willed his father to catch the ball. His father, who liked swift sharp ones in the gully but loathed the aching wait for a high skier, called bravely 'Mine!' and stationed himself underneath the plummeting ball. He stepped back a pace to adjust, and felt his ankle give at the moment the ball struck his cupped hands. Then he was on his back, an excruciating pain shooting up his leg, but with the ball still clutched to his chest. The field rang to a brilliant catch, but Paul Gauvinier came off on the arms of two fieldsmen and Peter had to help him home.

Mary Gauvinier saw them coming up the path, a curious couple, Paul, astride his bicycle but with his right leg held stiffly sideways away from the pedal, and Peter, aged eight, pushing from behind and grimly keeping up enough momentum to keep the cycle upright. 'It's nothing, Mary,' cried Paul as he saw the loving face twisted with anxiety. 'Just a sprain.'

'He was ever so brave, Mum,' called Peter. 'And he caught the catch. It was the highest one you've ever seen.'

He still thought of it that way, too, nearly forty years later, and he remembered the white strained face as his father nearly fainted from the pain. His mother bathed the swollen ankle with its greenish-purple bruise and held her husband's head against her breast and crooned, over and over, 'Just for a silly old catch, then. Just for a silly old catch.'

But why, he still wondered, had she put mustard in the water?

The chestnut trees were still there, of course, by now a dense green barrier some thirty feet high. They had given a brave display of white blossom in the spring, but now that was over, and a green curtain barred Gauvinier's view of the ground and its vital centrepiece, the wicket.

The cricket field had been a source of pride, argument and occasionally furious division in Tillingfold far longer than anyone could remember. The rival demands of cricket in the summer and football during the winter had never been satisfactorily resolved. In the euphoria of victory after the Second World War, the rival factions, the Parish Council, the Cricket Club and the Football Club had come to a welcome, if temporary, truce, and between them constructed the new brick pavilion. The Council's contribution was the bulk of the necessary money and an insistence on public toilets, one for 'gentlemen' and the other for 'ladies', to be constructed at either end. The Cricket Club, through the offices of Bason and Son, Builders, had provided the materials, the architect's plans and much of the electrical wiring. The Football Club, which contained most of the young men of the village within its ranks, did most of the building work. At the same time the cricketers spent all of one winter and most of the next summer digging up the 'square' and replacing its worn-out turf with new 'Cumberland' turf. They worked in relays, mostly at the week-ends, digging slightly off-centre in the playing field itself. This removed one major cause of friction. It allowed the footballers a reasonable width of pitch without having to encroach on the square, which could then be repaired, scarified, seeded and roped off from intrusive boots for the winter. They'd laid it properly, too, under the expert and ancient guidance of old Francis, the gardener up at the Hall. They dug out the ground to a depth of two feet and settled in a bed of hard core before bringing back the topsoil and laying the turf. They'd led off a wishbone of land drains, too, so not just the square but the whole field was usually quick to dry in the worst of winters; and finally they'd used the surplus soil to fill in a hollow that had made outfielding a hazard at Tillingford for years. They covered that with the turf they'd taken from the old square.

While it lasted, the cooperation was of the sort that had won the war. Gauvinier was once unwise enough to speculate in public whether it had not been successful because the women had been kept out of it. The Women's Institute, the Mothers' Union, the Music Circle and the female-dominated Young Farmers Union were by tradition the village's organizing bodies, who took it in turn to run the annual fête, the flower show, Harvest Festivals (two – one for the Church of England the other for the Presbyterian Brotherhood), the sale of work, the Christmas show and the Easter parade for Tillingfold's three thousand souls. These events were each run with a surprising degree of efficiency, but each in its own compartment. Rivalry was intense and the lines of demarcation were clearly etched into the village society.

Colonel Sir Edgar Trine, MC, Justice of the Peace, chairman of the Parish Council, Rural District Councillor, and member of the County Council, had run the joint effort with military discipline and an easy competence. As he was chairman of the Cricket Club anyway, and a life vice-president of the Football Club, he had a heavy foot in both camps. Colonel Trine had been so encouraged by the project's success that he had agreed in 1951 to coordinate Tillingfold's contribution to the Festival of Britain. He should have known better. Twenty-five years later the reverberations could still be felt; fifty years of association with the village, a lifetime's army experience, a Military Cross, a knighthood and a large fortune proved of little assistance when dealing with seven different and implacably opposed female committees. Gauvinier, with Oliver Fanshawe, Fred Bason and old Tom Hunter the garage proprietor, had stood and applauded the Colonel as he'd stalked out of the village reading-room. A minute before, he'd risen to his feet, amid a babel of claim and counter-claim, question and cross-question, heated accusation and furious denial, and had bellowed at the full extent of his voice, 'Shut up!'

It was a voice that had commanded battalions and silenced sergeant-majors. It was part of the legend of the desert that it had once halted a German attack, when Bren guns and six-pounders had failed. But this was his finest moment. The tumult and the shouting had died.

'Ladies, this meeting is closed,' said Colonel Trine firmly, and he had marched in silence to the door. As it had swung to behind his retreating back the assembled company had heard two words.

'*Bloody* women!' said the Colonel. It had been at this point that Gauvinier and his companions had disgraced themselves by applauding and then fleeing through the door, before the combined wrath of forty-five women could fall on their luckless heads.

As the *County Times* courteously reported the following Friday: 'A lively meeting at the parish reading-room failed to come to a decision as to whether Tillingfold would take part in the Festival of Britain celebrations later this year.' Sometimes it seemed to Gauvinier that Tillingfold had changed not one jot since the turn of the century. *'Plus ça change, plus c'est la même chose'* was a favourite saying of those who were still known as 'gentry' in the village.

Inevitably, Tillingfold had grown somewhat in the past twenty years. The new housing estate, which had founded Fred Bason's fortune and which now bordered the cricket field to the north with its bare lines of redbrick maisonettes, was the most obvious manifestation. Two hundred more families lived there, but even so, the ugly angular houses with their box-like rooms were mainly occupied by young married couples from Tillingfold itself or from the surrounding villages. Tillingfold was unlike Crawley, grown into a New Town, with its own industry, and designed to serve the whole complex of London's second airport at Gatwick; nor had it followed Horsham, willing recipient of 'overspill' businesses from the capital. Horsham, the southern bastion of the commuter belt; an historic and cosy township ruined forever by the town-planners; its heart ripped out, perverted to do obeisance to the motor-car and the supermarket; the green fields and wooded lanes of its environs transformed into a property developer's paradise.

There was no particular reason why Tillingfold should have

been spared the full impact of the twentieth century, just as there was no compelling reason why the village had ever existed there in the first place. It had never been a market town; it was too far from London and too far from the coast to be an urban retreat or a holiday dormitory. It had no railway station, no Town Hall, no village green. Over the centuries it had been tucked there in its own fold of the Downs, serving the big houses and estates scattered around it, supplying them with servants and service, bacon and bread and baked beans. Now, many of the landed families had gone and the estates had broken up, the pretentious mansions turned into conference centres, health hydros, or hotels. But even in the seventies these required provisions and cooks and maids and gardeners and butlers and waiters, just as the farms required mechanics and milkmen and technicians as well as tractor-drivers. If Tillingfold was no richer than the rest of Sussex, already the second richest county in England, then it certainly wasn't that much poorer.

Down on the 'new' housing estate (it was only fifteen years old), Gauvinier could see the cream-topped orange-sided milk-float edging like a rather slow ant along the rows of houses. *'Plus ça change ...'* He grinned to himself. Nothing changed, except that the horse had given way to the petrol-engine, which had in turn succumbed to quieter electricity, so that late-risers need not be disturbed by the coming of the milkman. It intrigued him that milk still had to be delivered before breakfast, even in these days of refrigerators. For in 1976 even the meanest of Tillingfold's cottages possessed a 'fridge' as well as a television set. Most also had some form of central heating, even if it was on the 'never-never' from the Gas Board, or the Electricity Board, or from Currys or the Co-op. And you hid the fact if your 'Teevee' was still only in black and white. Tillingfold was definitely A-B viewership these days, Gauvinier thought, lapsing mentally into 'media-jargon'.

The sight of the milk-float set him wondering. This was Wednesday morning. If Joe Deacon was delivering milk today, his shift pattern ended on Friday. He must try to see him, to forestall the otherwise inevitable Friday night binge with the boys. Joe Deacon behind the stumps was normally one of the most feared club wicketkeepers in the country. Even if he'd been on duty at the dairy since four-thirty in the morning. But when he turned up with a hangover, as seemed to be happening more frequently since his wife had given birth to their second daughter, he was as likely to lose a match as to win it. Gauvinier had had to fight quite strongly at the committee meeting the previous evening to include him in the team for the Raveley match.

Gauvinier put a hand into his pocket and pulled out the list he'd typed last night before going to bed. He usually dropped it in at the *County Times* office on his way to the station. Tillingfold maintained the old tradition of placing the team lists for the week-end matches (the village now ran a Sunday as well as a Saturday XI) in the Post Office window and also on the pavilion door; but in modern times the real medium for communication was the local newspaper. You could never trust them, however, to put the announcement in the 'Teams for Tomorrow' section on Friday, unless you delivered the thing personally. Even by post there was an even chance of its being lost among the 'small-ads'. They were even worse about accounts of the matches. Even one like this week's, the gala anniversary clash with the traditional rivals, and a fair crowd present, would not be covered unless Gauvinier or someone else connected with the club did not send in a 'write-up'. Once more tradition had it that the home club supplied the report, which was then subject to the unpredictable blue pencil of the *County Times*'s sub-editor and the exigencies of space on the sports pages.

Gauvinier looked at the list, in alphabetical order.

'Tillingfold (versus Raveley): Saturday, 15 July. 2.30 at Tillingfold. F. Bason, W. Budgeon, J. Deacon, P. Gauvinier (capt.), F. Hunter, A. Jess, J. Mitterman, N. Smith, R. Trine, C. Verrall, P. White.'

It wasn't a bad team, he thought. But was it good enough to beat Raveley in the most important game of the whole season? Not for the first time, Gauvinier had made up his mind that this must be his last year as Tillingfold captain, and he desperately wanted to go out on a high note. Oliver Fanshawe had gone back through all the records that could be found and had discovered that of the one hundred and thirteen recorded matches between the two teams forty-nine had been won by Raveley, forty-eight by Tillingfold, while sixteen had been drawn. Fanshawe had written a short article about the match which the *County Times* had promised to print on Friday in which he'd revealed that only once had either side scored over two hundred in the match and in all that time only one batsman – one Stovold, in 1891 – had scored a century. They were the sort of statistics beloved by cricketers and particularly, thought Gauvinier with a sudden pang, by ex-cricketers like his lifelong friend Fanshawe, whose playing days had been ended when a Messerschmitt's shell had burst in the cockpit of his Spitfire in the summer of 1940. A broken back had interfered neither with his friendship for Peter nor with his love of the game. He still stood as umpire, a gaunt immovable figure at the wicket every Saturday, feared and respected throughout the Weald. There wasn't a bowler in the county (or batsman, for that matter) who'd challenge the man who'd no-balled Greig, the England captain, and given out Hampshire's Barry Richards lbw off the second ball in the same charity match.

Gauvinier grinned, folded his piece of paper and strode off down the hill to his breakfast. If this weather would hold, and there was no sign at all that he could see of its breaking, then Saturday's match would be a cracker. By jingo, it would!

Chapter 2

The Opener

At about the same time as Gauvinier descended from the down, a shell-pink Rolls-Royce Corniche, its hood up against the early morning chill, slipped silently off the A24 and headed along the narrower tree-lined by-road towards Tillingfold. Albert Jess, driving casually with one hand, used the other to flick a black cigarette between his lips, depress the dashboard lighter, pull down the sun visor, insert a new tape in the stereo and light a cigarette, all with easy coordinated movements.

The morning sun lit up his golden hair and outlined his pale classical profile at the same time as it revealed a smattering of silver and an etching of lines about the corners of the eyes and mouth. Three years ago Albert Jess had been the brightest star in the pop firmament, the natural successor to the Beatles. Across the western world, no fewer than five million fans, according to Olympus Records Inc, had gone to bed each night dreaming they'd wake up to find Jess between the sheets with them. Unlike some of his fellow-performers, Jess had not sampled more than four or five of the five million, and then in reasonable privacy. His only liaison that had made the headlines had been immortalized in one of the more waspish gossip columns: 'Jess, the soon-to-be ex-pop singer, is now reported to be serenading Petronella Solario, the lissom Brazilian violinist. No doubt a guitarist can make sweet music on a G-string, but the news will sadden the faithful five million who've so far refused to acknowledge that their idol is nearer forty than thirty, nearer five feet than six, and much, much nearer Miss Solario most nights (and mornings) than they'll ever be.'

Jess, five feet three inches, aged thirty-eight, had lost his temper for the last time in his career. He sought out the columnist at a literary luncheon at the Savoy the same day.

'I hear you've been writing about me,' he said, shaking hands. The columnist looked down at him from his well-groomed six feet three inches. 'Anything troubling you, dear boy?' he inquired, raising both eyebrows.

'Nothing much. Every single word in your article was true,' said Jess, and kicked him, hard, on the right knee-cap. The columnist went down with a sudden cry of rage and pain. Jess kicked him on the left knee-cap and walked to the door through the astonished party.

'I'm sorry to spoil a lovely show,' he said apologetically to his hostess. 'I should have kicked him in the balls, but I don't think he's got any.'

Then he had left.

He told Gauvinier three years later, 'It cost me £10,000 for damages, but it was worth every penny.' He had disbanded his group, sacked both his manager and his agent, cancelled all his tours and scrapped his recording contract.

'That cost me another million,' he said. 'They all called me mad. But I'd have gone mad if I'd carried on. So I retired, and within six months they'd forgotten all about me. Now I don't even have to sign autographs any more. And I can join the club without being a nuisance to anyone.'

Jess took his retirement seriously. As Albert Jeavons, he'd driven with his dad from Raveley every year for the annual cricket match, and he'd always coveted the lovely old Tudor farmhouse on the outskirts of Tillingfold. He hadn't made a fuss about it. He'd just bought it when it came up on the market, along with five acres of market garden, a hundred or so more acres of farmland and a small Jersey milking herd. And then he set about teaching himself to farm, just as he'd taught himself to play the guitar.

Young Trine had handled the deal. It amused Jess to give the orders to Trine, but he hadn't made a meal of it, and the double garage had been built, the swimming pool constructed (with its Spanish surround) and the staff engaged in a remarkably short time. Tillingfold had absorbed the pop star and his exotic companions with as little commotion as it had accepted the movie idol, the financier and the transatlantic diamond smuggler, that had preceded him as owners of Birdwood Manor.

'It takes all sorts to make the world' is a favourite saying of the Tillingfold villagers, which doesn't stop them gossiping like mad, and they found in Jess a welcome new subject for comment, discussion, censure and speculation.

But the 'comings and goings' at Birdwood began to die down as Jess grew away from the London scene, as the visits of his more outlandish friends and acquaintances grew more infrequent.

'Why didn't you emigrate, find a haven, or something like that?' Gauvinier had asked him.

'It was Mickey Mouse money. It didn't mean a thing to us. We just earned it and spent it. We were lucky our manager was straight. Plenty weren't. We could have been rooked left, right and centre. It was thanks to Ed I was able to get this place; according to him, I can keep it going until the cows come home – sorry, no pun meant – on the record royalties, whether the farm makes money or not. I'm quite happy to stay in England. I had more than ten years on the road and it was great – money, all the birds, travel. But I found out it didn't mean anything. I just wanted to get back to England and, well, this.' He waved an arm towards the window.

'What made you pack it all up?'

'I think it was Petronella. She's fabulous – a real star. She made me realize that I didn't know a thing about music really – the guitar was the only thing I could play and she picked it up the first time I took her home and made me look like a three-year-old mental defective. I was mad at the time, but it made me think. The more I thought the more unhappy I got with the whole show – the gigs, the girls, the travel and the noise – the bloody *bloody* noise. It was either pack up or the fruit cage for me. So I kicked old wotsisname and the whole lot at the same time.'

'D'you miss it?'

'Sometimes, I suppose. But it was ninety per cent razzmatazz, nine per cent hard work and one per cent talent. It was enough for a bit, but in the end it was killing me. In this business, it's only the cows that stink, and you can wash that off.'

The Wicketkeeper

'Morn', Mrs Danbury.'

'Morning, Joe. Four pints this morning please. We've got Daisy coming this afternoon with our William.'

'That'll be nice, Mrs Danbury. Bill still playing cricket, then?'

'No, he doesn't get much chance with that new job, and the baby and all.'

'Don't I know it. G'morn', Mrs Danbury.'

'Thank you, Joe.'

'Mornin', Joe. You're late today. Usually pass you in the High Street.'

'Bloody bottling machine broke down at the depot. Finished your paper-round, then?'

'Aye – must get back for me breakfast else me mum'll belt me . . . Playing this week-end then?' [Diffidently.]

'Dunno. Ain't 'eard what the selection committee decided. Met last night, didn't they?'

'Yup. Up "The Red Lion" as ever. Saw skipper this morn', walking up down way before six-thirty, large as life.'

'Huh. 'Sall right for them as can afford it.'

'Hey, Joe, hear you got two stumpings last week at Billington.'

'Uh-uh. Dropped a catch, though.'

'Cor . . . bet it was a difficult one down the leg side, Joe. You'll make up for it on Saturday.'

'You belt off, young Bobby, or your mum'll give you what for. Can't stand here gossiping all day. Now where did I put that pencil, then?'

'Behind your ear, Joe. Cheers. See you Saturday.'

'Bloody kids . . . that 'un's not so bad though. Oh. Morning, Mr Gauvinier.'

'Morning, Joe. Wanted to have a word with you. Not holding you up, I hope?'

'Dunno what the world's coming to if a bloke can't stop for a chat now and then, Mr Gauvinier.'

'Indeed. You had a good game last week. That leg-side stumping was one of the slickest I've ever seen.'

'Ah, but I dropped that other 'un. That Jones – that made seventy odd. We'd 'a won the game but for that.'

'Oh I don't know, Joe. You never can tell, in cricket. You hadn't got your eye in that soon in the game.'

'I was suffering a bit anyway, Guv'nor.'

'Ah yes, well. It happens to all of us. I say, Joe, this weather's just the thing, isn't it. D'you think it'll hold for Raveley on Saturday?'

'Bound to, Guv'nor. That's a good match, Raveley. They've got those two Pakkies, haven't they?'

'Yes, indeed. We'll all of us need clear heads if we're to beat those blighters ... How's the family? Wife all right after your last?'

'She's doing nicely, thank'ye, Guv'nor.'

'What was it this time, Joe? Boy or girl?'

'Girl this time – makes two of each.'

'Great. That's a big family, these days. Joe, if you'll ring the bell this morning when you get round to us my wife'll let you have a few things she's had kept by. They may help a bit ... you know ... and there's no hope of us having any grandchildren now, it seems.'

'It don't matter.' [Mumbling] 'We're all right.'

'Lord bless us, you'll be doing us a favour, Joe ...'

'Joe Deacon, where you bin all mornin' ... We're awaitin' our milk still and it's gone half past ...'

'Sorry Joe, I must be off. Get you the sack ... It's all my fault, Mrs Larkins ... keeping Joe gossiping here. Yes, cricket again, I'm afraid. 'Bye Joe. See you tonight.'

'Righto, then, Guv'nor. And – er – thanks a lot.'

'Don't think another thing about it, Joe.'

'Sorry, Mrs Larkins. What can I do you for this morning?'

'Cheeky bugger ... you wouldn't get the chance. Two pints please, Joe, and take your eyes off.'

'It's a bit difficult, Mrs ... but it's a bit much this time of the morning. Ta-ra.'

'Ta-ra Joe ... Oh, how's your Sally?'

'Doin' fine, ta. Morning, Mrs Smith.'

'Morning, Joe, four pints please ... Ta very much.' [Confidentially] 'Joe, can you do us a favour, then?'

[Suspiciously] 'What's that?'

'Could you keep an eye on our Norm on Saturday. It's his first game with the team – Mr Gauvinier phoned last night to tell him – and he's ever so young, really, and ...'

'Never you worry, Mrs Smith. Thought you was goin' to ask me to hold the bill over till next week. I'll watch Norm – not that he needs any. He's a big lad now, you know. I'll keep an eye on him. But you tell him not to try to bowl too fast now. Get 'em on a length and I'll stop 'em if the batsman doesn't. Must go, I'm all behind, like the cow's tail. Ta-ra, then.'

And so Joe Deacon, milkman, wicketkeeper, husband and would-be-rake, received homage, a warning, a handout, an invitation and a commission; all before eight o'clock on a fine Wednesday morning in July.

The Fast Bowler

Two weeks before, Norman Smith, aged sixteen and nine months, had bent low over his desk in the examination room of Billington Comprehensive School and completed his last O-level examination paper. It happened to be on social history and the question – 'Examine the place of women in nineteenth-century society' – had given him just the chance he needed to use a quotation he'd come across browsing in the library only a few days earlier.

'Lord Byron,' wrote Norman Smith, 'not only qualified as the nineteenth century's number one male chauvinist pig but also accurately pin-pointed the place of women in nineteenth-century society when he wrote:

'"... Ye Lords of Ladies intellectual

"Inform us truly, have they not hen-pecked you all?"'

Hoping he'd quoted the poetic peer accurately, and that the examiner would be a man, Norman Smith ruled a neat double line across the page, put his pen in his pocket, handed in his paper and cycled the seven miles home to Tillingfold.

That evening he confronted his parents. The Smiths always had high tea as soon as his father returned from the grocer's shop that he'd managed for the past fifteen years.

'I'm not going back to school.'

Mr Smith looked up from his plate of ham.

'You're not what?'

'Oh Norman, how can you say such a thing?' Mrs Smith wailed. She often wailed; Mr Smith was not an easy man to please.

'I'm not going to school.' Norman said it calmly, but his stomach was screwed into a knot of anticipation.

'Oh yes you are,' said his father, rising slowly to his feet and beginning to unfasten his belt. 'Else I'll thrash the living daylights out of you.'

'Norman, no ...' Mrs Smith could have been addressing either of them. They both had the same name. But they took no notice.

'You're never going to belt me, ever again,' said Norman, standing up too. Mr Smith was six feet tall and broad with it but Norman was still able to look down at his father, being three inches taller.

'I'm going to get a job. I've done what you wanted. I've sat my exams and I'm not going to do any more.'

'You must be daft.' Mr Smith sat down. 'Let's talk this over sensibly.'

Norman knew he'd won. The following morning he took his bicycle and rode up to the Clinghammer stables to put his proposition to Harry Broome, the head lad.

'I want a job, Mr Broome. My dad wants me to go on and take my A-levels, and then join one of the big grocery firms.' He shuddered. 'I couldn't stand it. I feel sort of awkward at school – I'm too big.'

'All I want to do is to work with horses. I've always liked

them, and they seem to know I do. I'll never be a rider, I'm too big, but I want to learn every single thing I can about them.'

He grinned. 'It's either that or cricket. I reckon if I work for you Sunday mornings instead of Thursday afternoons, then I'll be able to play for Billington Thursdays and Tillingfold Saturdays and Sundays. I don't reckon on a county trial for at least twelve months yet, and at least I'll have started to learn a trade.'

Harry Broome nodded. He liked a boy to know his own mind, even if young Smith seemed just a little too cocksure. Gauvinier had told him of the lad's promise as a fast bowler ('and, by God we need one at the moment'), and that the county coach wanted him for the under-nineteens next year, but not before.

'All right,' he said. 'Start seven sharp in the summer, eight in the winter. That way you can knock off at midday for your cricket whenever you like. Fifteen quid a week until you're seventeen and we'll see how you work.'

Already, a fortnight later, it was a success. Young Smith was immediately popular with the other stable lads. He was huge, and therefore didn't pose any threat to them in their careers as jockeys. He was very strong, and took on much of the heavy work around the stables, like humping straw bales and mucking out. And he had a way with horses. Even the most difficult thoroughbred turned gentle under his huge hands.

That Wednesday, he'd gone along to the nets at the Cricket Club. Gauvinier had spotted him (at six feet three inches he was hard to miss) standing shyly back.

'Evening, Norman, want to join in?'

He was a little surprised, although he'd known about his keenness since the lad was little. Reports coming back from school were very encouraging, and that dedicated little bunch who ran the county's representative youth teams were enthusiastic. It was amazing how widely the county cast its net. Kenneth Carr, whose entire spare time was devoted to running the under-fifteen XI had rated Smith 'promising, very promising indeed'.

Norman had explained that he'd left school and joined the

stables, and now would like to play for the village, 'if I'm good enough'.

Gauvinier had sent him to put on his boots, and then, off a fifteen-pace run, he'd clean bowled Edward Trine twice in his first ten balls. Gauvinier put on some pads himself. His first ball from Smith reared uncomfortably but safely off the pitch short of a length. He played back to the second, feeling the ball thud into the bat much earlier than he'd expected. The third was a swinging full toss on the body, which Gauvinier whacked into the legside netting with a will, calling 'four' as he tossed the ball back. The boy went back to his mark. The next ball was straight, on a length, and Gauvinier, playing confidently forward, realized a fraction too late that the boy had held it back a trifle. The ball looped off the full face of the bat in a gentle arc back into Smith's hands.

'Well bowled,' Gauvinier called, feeling some chagrin. Fred Bason, waiting for his turn to bat, chuckled. 'Always was a bit too forward, and not only in cricket, either,' and ducked as Gauvinier drove the next, a slow half-volley, hard and straight at him.

The week-end before Norman Smith had played his first match for the Sunday XI, taking two wickets for thirty runs. Now he was included in the team to meet Raveley, because Tillingfold's regular opening bowler, John Burgess, was on holiday with his family and the usual reserve had a broken finger.

'Although,' as Fred Bason said, 'he's a right arm bowler and he's bust the little finger of his left hand, so why can't he play?'

In any case, young Norman had his chance. And Gauvinier, who was always inspired by keenness in others, rejoiced in his heart.

The Secretary

As he did every other morning of the year, James Mitterman, chartered accountant, folded back the sheet and the blanket covering him to a precise forty-five degrees. Only the slight indentation on the pillow betrayed the fact that he had slept there for the past eight hours.

Slipping on his paisley-patterned dressing-gown, he listened a moment at his wife's door before making his way to the bathroom to perform his ritual ablutions. The warm sun, flooding through the opaque window, caused him to pause and open the casement, just in time to catch the newspaper boy (James could never remember their names) riding up the circular tarmac drive. The lad caught the movement at the window.

'Sorry, Mr Mitterman – No *Financial Times* again today. Brought you *The Times* instead.'

'Thank you.' Mitterman inclined his head gravely. Sometimes he considered the inconvenience of living in the country hardly worth its benefits. Slowly he divested himself of his pyjamas, noting with approval the matching green against the dressing-gown. Really, Marks and Spencer did a fine job these days. Mitterman, for all his immaculate habits, was never ashamed of saving money. He bent to his daily exercises.

Thc grandmother clock in the hallway (by Joseph Windmills, Master of the Clockmakers' Company) chimed a quarter to seven as Mitterman trod softly down the carpeted stairs. He'd considered carefully, as he always did, before buying it. He'd preferred the grandfather he'd been offered, mainly because it was by Tompion, a name with more prestige, but had finally rejected it, as it would have been out of proportion in the hall at Little Standings.

Mitterman had his tea delivered quarterly by Fortnums. He and his wife preferred the Queen Mary flavour. He made it in a Queen Anne octagonal teapot and stood drinking it while he cast his eye over the business section. After ten minutes' wait for Winifred's tea to draw (she preferred several things stronger than he did), he carried a cup to her bedroom.

'My dear, I shall leave early this morning, if it will not put you out.' He was always courteous. 'I wish to be back in time for the practice this evening.'

Cricket was his one relaxation, even though his grave presence at the crease or in the field inclined on cloudy days to cast a chill over the most festive occasion.

'Very well, dear,' replied Winifred demurely, making a note that her 'sitting' must be over correspondingly early. James would have been surprised, not to say distressed, to learn what was happening, but there was no doubt that she and Angus Redfearn, ARA, were getting on famously. The picture, when it was hung the following year, caused a sensation.

Leaving early for Mitterman meant stepping into his BMW 2000 at ten past seven, then twenty minutes in the car to Billington Station, and a seat on the seven thirty-five fast train to Victoria. There was no need for him to show his season ticket at the station entrance. They knew well he travelled on a first-class season ticket (yearly cost, £745), bought always on 2 January, in cash.

Once he was comfortably ensconced in his compartment Mitterman opened his briefcase, took out a file, and settled to drafting next year's fixture list for Tillingfold Cricket Club. This was one of the reasons why he'd volunteered to become secretary/treasurer ... it occupied the spare hour or so he had on his way to his office, and, dare it be said, he knew deep within himself that he needed the Cricket Club very nearly as much as the Cricket Club needed him. Since he'd taken over as Hon. Secretary, the club's fixtures were up to date, their subscriptions paid in time, and their annual general meetings a model of propriety, if, as Gauvinier sometimes said to himself, a little dull. And by such methods the Mittermans grew nearer, they felt, to taking part in village life.

For it was a fact that James Mitterman was very good at running other people's money, even if his own affairs might not stand too close an inspection; just as it was equally true that he was a far better club secretary than he was an opening bat. Mitterman, who was invariably honest with himself, if not with his clients, privately admitted that the real reason he did the job was that it ensured him a place in the side. Gauvinier, transparently honest with everyone, put him in first on the theory that Mitterman could do less damage to Tillingfold's often shaky batting there than if he went in further down the order. In any case, Tillingfold Cricket Club needed a competent business mind just as much as it needed a good opening bat, and to those opponents who didn't know better, Mitterman *looked* a cricketer. His portly figure, immaculately pressed flannels, brightly shining white pads and pipe-clayed boots gave the immediate impression that Tillingfold meant business.

His highest score in the three seasons he'd been opening the batting was twelve. But in the same time the Club's bank balance had moved from being £95 overdrawn to a comfortable £150 'in the black'.

The Slogger

Young Trine, as four generations of Trine sons up at the Hall had been known, prepared for the day in his own style. As the sun touched his eyelids, he sat up in bed, yawned and then rolled upright towards the open window, taking in great breaths of the morning air. Stretching, he turned and saw that although his abrupt exit had not wakened his companion, it had pulled the sheet half away from her. She lay on her front, one leg slightly drawn up, her bottom thrust into the air. It was this bottom that was exposed, brown and smooth and inviting. It asked to be smacked. Young Trine smacked it.

'Come on, then, Helga, or Margaretta, or whatever you're called. Up, up, up. It's no good being an au pair if you're not going to get the tea in the morning. Up, up, up. The Colonel will be panting for you. Or I will.'

Ingrid Pettersen yawned, turned over on to her back and stretched, oblivious of the fact that the sheet no longer covered any of her.

'Edward,' she said, yawning, 'you're a bastard.'

She eased herself off the bed, timing the moment precisely to avoid his dive for her, and retreated with dignity to the door.

'Hey, you can't go around like that,' he said suddenly, realizing she was opening the door.

'Why not?' she said, opening it quickly and moving out on to the landing. She peeped back into the room. 'Nor can you, big boy.'

Edward grinned to himself, calculating that all hell would be let loose if his mother found her, and none at all if his father did. Even at seventy-five the old boy had a twinkle in his eye, thought Edward, turning on the shower in his own private bathroom.

As he showered and shaved, he had time to reflect that life in the seventies, for all its problems, wasn't so bad for an anachronism called Edward Trine. Marlborough, Oxford and now a directorship with the biggest land agents in the country had prepared him for a life of ease just as it had his father and his father's father before him.

Even in the seventies, with a Labour government, nationalization, taxation at the limit, comprehensivization (Edward gave a well-bred shudder at the word) and the trade unions, the Trines and their like still managed to hold out. They'd had to sell or let off most of the estate, except the house, the stables and about twenty acres, which was just as well, he thought. He couldn't see himself running the farm and paying the workers and generally acting like a feudal baron. With the best will in the world, and young Trine had plenty of that, he could see no reason why the situation shouldn't continue for another three or four generations. Even if death duties clobbered the old man's fortune, as they probably would, the estate agents and others (Christie's had offered him a 'directorship' to look out for old paintings among ailing old families, and nearer home Bason's wanted him on their board) would keep him well enough to maintain the Hall and any number of Ingrids, not to say the Mercedes, his hunting and his cricket.

'Coming, Mother,' he called down the stairs as he fastened his silk tie and trod hastily into grey suède Gucci shoes.

'I don't want to be late today. I've got a man coming in early to the office and I want to drop off my cricket boots at Budgeon's.'

'Yes, dear,' said Lady Trine placidly as young Trine accepted a plate of bacon and eggs from Ingrid, who brushed her breast against his shoulder as she set the plate in front of him.

'And if you must entertain the au pair in your room,' she continued in precisely the same tone of voice, 'I'd be obliged if you wouldn't make so much noise in the morning. It upsets your father.'

'Yes, Mother,' said young Trine, meekly. Sir Edgar coughed into his moustache, turning pink, and Ingrid smiled sweetly and swept out, carrying all before her.

The Last Man

The church clock struck nine o'clock as Bill Budgeon unlocked the door of his little workshop, took out a short pole with an s-hook at the end and pulled down a canvas shade to keep the sun off the display window. The modest sign over the premises said 'Budgeon – Shoemaker', and to the occasional inquirer Bill would explain patiently that leather, just as much as bacon or chocolate or material or anything else, was affected by the sun, and left in a south window, would dry and fade and even crack within a few months.

A low shelf in the window displayed just three pairs of men's shoes. Each was hand-sewn, one black, one a rich chestnut brown and the third white. They had each taken Budgeon a week to make during the slack summer season when repairs were few, and the price tags below them indicated the value Budgeon placed on his own work: £40; £55; £35. He rarely sold any hand-made footwear these days. His living, such as it was, came from repair work, and he made ends meet by grossly over-charging the gentry and under-charging the less well-to-do. Bill Budgeon knew that even in these days of the munificent Welfare State it was no fun being poor. When he was eight, he'd gone down with polio – he'd never been vaccinated against the disease because his father hadn't believed in all this new-fangled medicine. Now, twenty years later, he lurched through life with one leg four inches shorter than the other and both bent outwards from the knee, which meant that his normal walk was a crab-like pigeon-toed shuffle. He refused to use a stick, and rode a bicycle with a fixed gear, from which he'd removed the right pedal, so that his good leg, the left, might propel the machine without interruption from the right. Because of this, and because he lived in perpetual pain, he received a disability pension from the State, some £25 per week while he was single, increasing to £35 if he were ever to get married. But what the generosity of the politicians intended was confounded by the illiberality of the bureaucrats who came eventually to administer the law, as many old age pensioners and others had discovered. By some interpretation of the regulations that Budgeon had long ceased trying to understand, for every penny he earned per week over £25, his pension was correspondingly reduced.

This morning there were two official-looking envelopes among the usual batch of trade circulars in the little letter-box behind the shop door. Budgeon pitched the circulars unopened into a rubbish-bin beneath his workbench, and sat painfully on his high cobbler's stool to open the letters. The first, with its ominous 'OHMS' underlined in black and its official date-stamp, he turned over in his large stained hands. He took a curved leather knife and slit the envelope along the fold, his fingers neat and quick.

Dear Sir,

It is regretted that we appear not to have received a reply to our communication VAT/BB 12408 of 28 June 1976 and previous communications. Unless a satisfactory return of your business income for the past two years ended 1 April 1976 is made within seven days of the date of this letter, then we regret it will be necessary to institute criminal proceedings against you under VAT regulation 425 of 1974.

Yours faithfully,
E. M. Pledger
(for) HM Inspectors of Value Added Tax.

Budgeon read the letter twice, carefully. He rubbed his right knee, which seemed to be hurting more than usual, and then placed the letter with several others similar in a wooden box under the counter. He turned to open the next one.

As he slit the envelope the shop door opened with its compulsive 'ping' from the old brass bell above it, and young Trine stepped in and out of the sunshine with a cheery, 'Morning Bill. How's business? Booming, I hope.'

'Morning, Mr Trine,' Budgeon liked 'Squire's son', as he'd always thought of him. His unfailing cheerfulness was infectious, even though it was founded in the sort of security Budgeon would never know. At least young Trine meant no harm to anyone, which was more than you could say for some folk.

'Can you fix these for me?' He tossed the white shoes on to the counter. They were studded and of a curious design – neither shoes nor boots, but slightly raised at the heel to support the ankle. Budgeon had designed and made them himself for Trine. 'I want them for the nets tonight, if you can manage.'

Budgeon examined the boots. There wasn't much wrong with them – the stitching had started to come apart at the left instep. He grunted.

'Cost you two quid.'

'All right, you old robber. They're really out of this world, to wear. By the way, did you get any reply from those patent people?'

'Nothing yet, just the bloody tax people after me to spoil a decent day. OK, Mr Trine, I'll have these ready for you – I'll bring them down the nets myself tonight.'

'Thanks, Bill, that's good of you.' He went out, the door pinging to behind him. Bill Budgeon opened his second envelope.

Dear Mr Budgeon,

Thank you for your interesting letter and enclosure of one pair of cricket boots, which we have retained for further inquiries.

At first sight, it appears that your invention of an ankle-supporting cricket boot could well be subject to patent, although further investigations will have to be made before a patent can be issued.

If you wish to pursue your application further, I would be grateful if you would complete the enclosed form in the fullest detail possible; and I would point out that a cheque for £50 should accompany the form to cover the cost of processing your application.

Yours sincerely,
A. D. St John Harrington
(for) HM Office of Patents.

'Oh well,' said Bill Budgeon to himself, 'that's what squire's son wanted to know. I'll tell him at nets tonight. But where the hell I can find £50 I'm damned if I know.'

He thought of the VAT letter and his knee ached again. Then he thought of the nets, and the Saturday match against Raveley, and forgot the pain. He fitted a child's shoe on to his last and began to strip the sole from the upper. So long as there was cricket, even the tax man could take a running jump.

The Pavilion

Gauvinier let himself into the pavilion just after six o'clock, though the weekly nets were not due to begin until six-thirty. He made it a habit to check over the club bag at least once a fortnight. Like everything else, the cost of cricket gear had risen beyond all proportion in the last few years. Now a top-rate cricket bat could cost over £20, a pair of pads over £10. Tillingfold Cricket Club had managed to keep the cost of playing membership down to £5 a head (£2 if you were under eighteen, £1 if you were under sixteen) and in fact there were more non-playing 'vice-presidents' who paid £3 a year than there were playing members. But with at least two matches a week (these days, Tillingfold occasionally put out two teams on a Saturday as well as a Thursday XI) the wear on the equipment was immense.

Every annual general meeting for the past few years had struggled to balance rising costs with the necessity to keep membership fees low. As James Mitterman pointed out, you got an awful lot for your £5 membership when you reckoned that it cost £50 a year to belong to the Tillingfold Golf Club, with £25 joining fee on top of that, and green fees and the nineteenth hole as well, not to mention a couple of hundred pounds for your set of clubs.

'Surely it is not beyond the means of even the youngsters to afford a bat and a pair of pads today,' Mitterman had told the AGM, proposing that expenditure on the 'club bag' be limited to the provision of new balls for home matches and a 'box' for the club wicketkeeper only.

Gauvinier had been on his feet immediately. He believed

passionately that any such move would spell the death of the Cricket Club, and the end of something that had contributed enormously through the years to the unique quality of life a village like Tillingfold had to offer all its inhabitants. But he knew better than to try to express such philosophical arguments at the AGM.

'There's nothing to stop anyone using his own kit if he wants to,' he said. 'But if you want to turn Tillingfold into a "gentlemen only" team then you're setting about it the right way. There's been enough trouble over the years in the Club with that one, and we don't want any more of it than we can help.' He paused. 'You know as well as I do that there's not a lad in Tillingfold who can afford £20 for a cricket bat of his own. And precious few fathers either. But there are still plenty of parents who'll fork out a fiver to give their son a start in the game.'

Gauvinier looked round the meeting, at Sir Edgar Trine in the chair and at the secretary/treasurer.

'And with your permission, Mr Chairman, I would like to point out to my friend the proposer of the motion that if we adopt it as it stands it will be very difficult to play any cricket at all in future. If all the club bag were to contain, as the motion states, were to be new balls and a box, and no stumps or bails, not to say bats or pads or gloves or even umpires' coats . . .'

Loud laughter interrupted him, and the motion never found a seconder.

After more than twenty-five years of use, the 'new' pavilion was well worn in. It consisted of a simple oblong room, with wide windows and a central door looking out on to the pitch. A strip of coconut matting led round the long trestle table which took up the middle of the floor. This was there so that the players' studs would not damage the parquet flooring, but over the years most of it had become pockmarked like a darts board surround.

At both ends, the changing rooms led off, each with unpainted wooden lockers forming seats round three walls, and a bare table. There was access to one WC and one narrow wash basin, and the two dressing rooms were lit by high windows, through which, if he stood on the locker, a very tall man might look out at the field. It smelled, as all pavilions do, of stale sweat and (particularly after the football season) embrocation, old mud, of damp and of linseed oil. It was unlovely, and not very convenient, but it was home for Tillingfold CC.

Gauvinier, as he sorted out the pads into pairs and checked over the bats for damage, thought it was time the whole place had another coat of paint. He'd preferred the old pavilion, with its wide wooden shutters that opened upwards and were propped up by two long slats. True, they were a constant danger to anyone sheltering beneath them, as the slats were liable to be dislodged by small boys both by accident and design; and when the old building had been pulled down, there wasn't a timber in it that had no woodworm, or dry rot, or wet rot, or all three. But they'd kept the old scoreboard with its parallel runners, into which three sets of numbers fitted: total score, number of wickets down, the last man's score. The numbers themselves were painted on square metal panels, white figures on a black background; and way back in the past someone had devised a system whereby you turned over '0' to find '1', '2' to find '3', and so on. Someone else in a moment of Victorian humour had painted a little duck in the place of a '0' and this was reserved for Tillingfold's favourite sons and honoured enemies. A 'duck' was a form of affectionate accolade which it took many years to earn. Gauvinier merited one, for instance, and so did Bill Budgeon and Fred Bason. But Young Trine hadn't earned his yet, and nor had James Mitterman; so when they scored nothing, which was not unusual, the occasion was marked by a stark uncompromising '0'.

As long as Gauvinier could recall there had been an apparent surplus of '4s' and a shortage of '9s'. But he'd never yet found ninety-nine, nine, nine to be necessary, and although he'd many times sworn to do something about it, it was one of those items that always failed to find its way on to the agenda for the AGM.

Gauvinier placed the First XI kit in its huge leather travelling bag and stowed it back in its locker. He set four damaged pads (one pair and two odd ones) aside for Bill Budgeon to take away and repair, and he threw out two bats that were fit only for kindling. The rest of the gear he left out on the table for the evening's practice, together with half a dozen old balls of varying degrees of decrepitude. He kept a couple back. One, which had dismissed a set of visitors on a wet wicket for thirty-three, he reckoned would be good enough with a polish for another match. Another he wanted to save for young Norman Smith, who he calculated would be too shy to try to bag a 'good 'un'.

'I don't know,' he said in exasperation to Fred Bason, who'd just arrived. 'What some people do to the kit is beyond belief. Look at that . . . even in this day and age they're still knocking in the stumps with the face of the bat . . .'

'Oh, ar,' Fred answered thoughtfully, 'it takes all sorts . . .'

The Nets

By twenty to seven the nets were in full swing. Most of the team arrived around six-thirty, because they all in their own way appreciated the importance of the Raveley game to the Club. While Bason got the hand mower from the long lean-to behind the pavilion in his slow methodical way, Gauvinier and the other early-comers set up the nets. They chose a flat piece of the outfield under the chestnut trees (so the ball was hit away from the road into the empty field), and as Fred trundled the mower up and down the others erected the net with an easy skill born of long practice. Young Trine, one of the few all in white, swung the mallet with enthusiasm, knocking in the pegs for the guy ropes. Budgeon held one pole. A couple of village youngsters, eager to join in any way they could, grabbed the others – they'd be deep-fielding later on, tearing across the grass and hoping to be noticed for their keenness. Each pole was capped at the ends by an iron cup and a spike, and the thick tennis netting, sticky with creosote preservative, was already attached. Each roll was surprisingly heavy, and took two men to carry it from the lean-to. They had to be taken down after each practice and re-erected each time. The field wasn't large enough for the nets to remain in position while a match was in progress, and in any case, the village vandals (oh yes, Tillingfold had its vandals as the state of the public toilets behind each end of the pavilion testified) would have made short work of any property not left under lock and key.

Looked at from above, the nets made the form of a capital 'E', with four or five bowlers taking it in turns to bowl at the two batsmen. Gauvinier had made a point of asking Jess to come along, and was pleased to see that the former singer had turned up early. It was far better for the team if a newcomer were to introduce himself to them at the nets, rather than just to turn up to a match. That could create resentment, and holding the balance between such a cross-section of village society was a difficult task at the best of times. In this, he knew, he was not alone. Thousands of Club captains all over the country weekly curse the class divisions, which in spite of all the well-meant efforts to the contrary, not only continue but even appear to thrive on those very same efforts.

But if the established members of the side showed various degrees of diffidence in greeting the new member, Jess had no such inhibitions. He was in any case quite accustomed to receptions both frosty and hysterical, and he was enough of a cricketer to know that it was only with the bat and the ball that he would gain acceptance. So he threw himself into the practice, seizing a ball and hurling it down the wicket at Fred Bason, who whacked the slow full toss away to leg for what would have been a most comfortable four.

'Keep 'em there,' he called, patting the ball back down the net and grinning. And Jess replied, 'I'll get you next time, that was just a sighter,' knowing full well that he was not bowler enough to get anything past that broad bat, without a great deal of luck or lack of concentration on the batsman's part. But at the same time he felt that inner glow which kindles at the first signs of acceptance into a new society. And noticing a tall dark youngster standing apart at the back of the nets, he went up to him, tossing the ball between his hands, and said easily, 'Are you new too? I'm Albert Jess – come and join in. What do you do? Bowl?' And Gauvinier, delighted that his new capture seemed to be settling in so well, took the spare good ball from his pocket and tossed it to Norman, calling, 'Come on there, young man, and let's see what you're made of.'

The Tillingfold net rules were first come, first served, ten minutes each with the bat, and everyone expected to bowl. To this Gauvinier had added ten minutes' fielding practice for everyone at the end; he was so keen that to skipper a slack fielding side was genuine agony to him. It was the captain's duty to keep an eye on the ten-minute periods, and to nominate the next to bat. It could often become a delicate matter. He approached young Trine.

'Teddy, would you mind very much if I asked Jess to take next turn? I want to give him a good try-out and I want to put young Norman against him before they both get tired.'

'Okay, skipper. I don't need much practice this week anyway.' He was referring to the dashing forty-three he'd hit the previous week, and in any case his 'form' or lack of it worried him not in the slightest. He was only too happy to have a game.

Gauvinier turned to Jess. 'Pad up, if you wouldn't mind, Mr Jess. Help yourself from the bag. We want to get a good look at you.' Behind his back he heard a mutter, soft enough to be an aside but loud enough for him to hear. 'Bloody favouritism again. Just so long as it's money. Who *is* that funny little pouf?'

Gauvinier checked himself and gave no sign of hearing. He bent to field a smartly driven ball, straightened up with it and tossed it back to the bowler.

'Hullo, Frank.' [In genuine concern] 'What on earth have you done to yourself?'

Frank Hunter had just arrived, having strolled across after taking the pump levels for the evening and locking up the garage. He wore a blue suit which clashed with his bright red tie, just as his extreme left-wing political views contrasted with his strongly conservative nature, and, for that matter, his perpetual ill-temper with his basic sportmanship. All of which, like his bad teeth, he had inherited along with the garage and service station from Old Tom, his father. The Hunters had been thorns in Tillingfold's flesh, particularly the flesh of the cricket captain, for years. The cause of Gauvinier's exclamation was a new sling holding Hunter's left arm, with the wrist peeping from it swathed in bandages.

'Sprained it.'

'Will you be fit in time for Saturday? It's a real blow if you won't.'

'Can't really say.'

Frank Hunter had indeed twisted his wrist that afternoon working on a customer's lorry. But he was already regretting the bandage and the sling, for the sight and the sound of a cricket ball against bat always stimulated the strong, athletic side of him. The pleasure of needling Gauvinier hardly seemed worth the risk of eliminating himself from Saturday's game.

'Let me know as soon as you can, Frank. There's nobody else who can really take your place, you know. Have you been to the doctor?'

'Oh, it's not as bad as all that. Just rest it a couple of days and it'll be all right. Good shot, sir!'

Jess had picked a goodish ball off his toes and clipped it away with as neat an on-drive as could be wished. Frank Hunter hastened to qualify his admiration.

'Course, that's in the nets. It's a different matter to do it out in the middle.'

'True enough, Frank.' The two men watched Jess face up to the next ball, a fast one just short of a length, which reared up off a dent in the pitch and flew high off in the direction of gully. Jess dropped the bat and wrung his fingers in pain.

'No, no, it's all right.' He waved back the boy, who'd started up the pitch towards him. He picked up the bat gingerly and settled to his stance again.

'Ease off, Norman,' called Gauvinier. 'These nets aren't like the middle. We don't want anybody killed.' But although his concern was real, another part of him was hoping that on Saturday Smith would be able to whistle a few round the unprepared heads of the Raveley batsmen. His feelings were not so far different from those publicly expressed and deeply felt by the entire England team, captain and selectors, whose quest for a genuinely fast bowler had for years been unsuccessful.

'Last six. Next pair ready?' He called, setting the whole machinery of the nets in motion again. 'Joe, when you've had your knock I'd like you to put the gloves on. Our ground fielding and returns to you last Saturday were not too good at all.'

'Righto, Mr Gauvinier,' Joe Deacon was always delighted to be spoken to and enjoyed the routine of fielding practice, which made him feel important and very much needed. It was like being the hub of a great bicycle wheel. He stood in the centre with the players spaced round him, taking their returns with a flourish and tossing the ball to Bill Budgeon, who whacked it out with a bat, hard or softly, along the ground or in the air, as his fancy took him. It galled Budgeon not to be able to field in the deep, for he knew he was just as capable as young Paul White of sending back the ball flat and hard and right over the top of the stumps, like the West Indians did. Many spectators and opposing players had likened White in the field to Keith Boyce, the great West Indian all-rounder, and you could never say that of Bill Budgeon, with his crippled legs and lurching gait. It was more a marvel that he was able to play cricket at all.

As the shadows lengthened and the evening cooled, the rhythm of the practice faltered and died down. Fred Bason and Frank Hunter, who'd been persuaded to doff his sling for some fielding practice, went off to 'The Dog and Duck' for a well-earned pint, carrying Joe Deacon not too unwillingly along with them. Jess, nursing his right hand, with its middle finger already swelling and turning blue-red with the bruise, invited Gauvinier to 'sling his bike in the boot', and drove him off in the Rolls to Birdwood, for a large whisky and a lengthy discussion on Mahler. The rest of the team-members went their several ways to the sound of their ritual farewell calls.

'Night, Bill, thanks for the boots.'

'Night, Mr Trine.'

'Night, Fred. See you Saturday.'

'Not if I sees you first.'

'See you Saturday, Paul.'

'See, you, Norm. Good luck, Saturday.'
'Thanks, I'll need it.'
''S not you who'll need it. It'll be them Raveley blighters.'
'Night, all.'
'Night.'

Chapter 3

Gauvinier's private weather forecast was proved correct, much to his gratification. Saturday, like Wednesday and the intervening days, dawned misty; but by seven o'clock the sun had sucked away the mist and the Downs lay baking under yet another cloudless sky. It looked as though this might be the hottest day of the year, said the man from the 'Met' Office on Radio Four at five to eight. Gauvinier agreed, but he sniffed. His own opinion, which he offered free to anyone who cared to listen, was that the meteorological experts regularly forecast yesterday's weather for today, on the grounds that there was a fifty per cent chance of getting it right. But, he said to himself, as he breathed in the morning air, it would be a good day to win the toss, with the wicket rock hard with not a scrap of moisture. As Oliver Fanshawe always said, 'If you've got runs on the board, then it's up to the other side to get 'em.' And there was an equally important consideration so far as the older members of the Tillingfold side were concerned; fielding after tea, with the heat going out of the sun and the opportunity to back off into the cool of the chestnut trees as the shadows lengthened, was a darned sight more pleasant than sweating it out in the hot sun, when you might have had one too many pints at lunch-time, or be working off a heavy Saturday dinner. (In spite of long indoctrination by the BBC and the Women's Institute etiquette classes, Tillingfold still regarded the midday meal as 'dinner'. Lunch was something you had with your cup of tea at eleven or so; and in the evening there was 'high tea' or supper'.)

Invariably the first person to arrive at the cricket field on match days, apart from the Tillingfold squad of energetic small fry, who regularly failed to commit suicide on the swings, was Oliver Fanshawe.

As the umpire and honorary groundsman, it was his job to make sure the pitch was selected, cut, rolled and marked out, ready for the wickets to be pitched promptly at two o'clock, half an hour before the game. It was a duty he had performed rain or shine, every match day since he'd returned half-mended from the RAF Hospital near Leatherhead, without complaint and without thanks. He had insisted from the start that if he was thanked for doing something he very much wanted to do, he would cease forthwith. And as Fanshawe was not a man to be argued with, he had continued as he'd started.

Promptly at eleven-thirty, Fanshawe walked carefully to the door of the lean-to. He unlocked the old-fashioned padlock with a key he kept on a ring which swung from the chain suspended between his two waistcoat pockets. He pulled the hand-mower out for inspection. Tillingfold possessed three mowers – the little light twelve-inch 'pusher' for the wicket itself, a bigger motor-mower with a seat, which was used for a rough cut of the square and the few yards around it, and a piece of agricultural history which consisted of three overlapping sets of revolving blades attached to a pull-bar. Frank Hunter usually dragged it around the outfield twice a month, using his Land-Rover breakdown wagon. The clippings were left on the grass, sometimes making it quite difficult to hit a four to the long-on boundary.

Fanshawe examined the little mower carefully. He dusted a few old clippings from the bearings and, using a small spanner which he carried in his pocket, adjusted the height of the knife and the set of the revolving blades against it. Next he oiled the wooden rollers and gave each of the five nipples a shot from a small grease-gun. He gave a few experimental pushes to check the level of the cut and then, satisfied, pulled the mower out to the wicket.

There were some from visiting teams who said that old Fanshawe could select a wicket precisely suited to Tillingfold's needs, no matter what the weather – 'a sticky dog at one end and a bone-hard flyer at the other', as one visiting speaker had opened his speech at the annual dinner. In fact Fanshawe worked his square in strict rotation, moving across it from left to right, and then back to where the wicket had re-grown as the season had worn on. But he always kept the last wicket for the Raveley match. He had already cut it twice during the week, and after the nets he had persuaded a squadron of the hangers-on to push the heavy old horse-roller up and down it a half-dozen times. To the uninitiated the wicket appeared fit and ready for play; but Fanshawe now gravely mowed it yet again – up and back again in his own tracks, then he moved over and repeated the action six times; and then he repeated the whole process from the other end, until from the lush green of the square emerged a brown, immaculate twenty-two yards of near perfect wicket.

Fanshawe tipped the mower's box, which was half full of clippings, on to the heap at the side of the pavilion, and then rolled the pitch with the light roller. Up and down, up and down, six times again. By this time he was very hot. He had removed his jacket, his waistcoat and his tie, and was working in his braces with his sleeves rolled up.

'Morning, Oliver. You look like the original British navvy.'

'It would do that waistline of yours good to do a bit of labouring yourself, Peter.'

'Lord, I'd fade away altogether,' said Gauvinier, who was as thin as a rake. 'Let me give you a hand.' And, despite the protests, he ran to the lock-up shed and re-emerged carrying an oblong frame, a bucket of whitewash, an old plaster-brush and an expanding metal foot-rule. Between them they measured the pitch's twenty-two yards, marked out the creases with care and then stood back to admire their efforts. The whitewash dried instantly in the hot sun.

'My goodness, there'll be some runs in that today,' said Gauvinier.

'Depends on who's holding the bat,' said his friend, and they walked off together, it now being well past opening time, to consume a pint of the real ale that 'The Dog and Duck' had recently introduced for its more discerning customers.

Not unnaturally, their talk turned to the afternoon's match and its participants. It was an old theme, recurrent and familiar as a much-read book.

'I hope we give them a good game. Since the war they've got so strong I often think they feel it's beneath them to turn out their First XI against us. But we usually make them battle a bit. What d'you think of our new chaps?'

'We've got something there in young Norman. He's very quick off fifteen yards. I'd like to see what he can do off a full run.'

'Let him get his length and direction first. I know I'm old-fashioned, but it's not just speed that gets the Lillees and the Holdings their wickets. It's length and line and control. Look at Thomson. All flash and blather. He'll be finished in a couple of seasons, you mark my words. What about your teenagers' idol?'

Gauvinier grinned. 'He'll be all right. There's a lot to that young man that doesn't show.'

'And a blamed sight too much that does.'

'He can't help his good looks. Or the lines and the silver threads among the gold. He's got some class as a bat, though. And he didn't make any fuss about that rap on the knuckles. I think he'll settle down fine as soon as the blokes get to know him. At any rate, I like him,' he ended emphatically.

'And what the skipper says goes, of course.' He paused, for Gauvinier to digest the gentle rebuke.

'Oh Lord, I know I'm too arrogant. But this prejudice against a new player, or anyone who comes to the village from outside, gets my goat. Heaven knows, I still feel like a rank outsider and I've been here forty-seven years. It's all this yackety yack that gets you down.'

'Oh?' he asked dryly. 'I think they know you by now, Peter. How's Frank's wrist? You shouldn't let him get under your skin, you know.'

'Did it show that much?' He continued ruefully, 'I haven't heard, so I'm hoping that no news is good news. He's so bloody exasperating, though, as though we're doing ourselves a favour persuading him to play. And yet really he loves it and wouldn't miss a game for the world.'

'There's nobody I would rather be with when my back is to the wall, though.'

'Especially when you're getting stick from *The Times*, eh, Oliver?'

This was a reference to a famous controversy. Oliver Fanshawe was a cricket fanatic. He kept all one hundred and thirteen editions of *Wisden's Cricketers' Almanac* in his library, together with his own extensive records of Tillingfold and Sussex. He knew by heart every one of the forty-seven laws of cricket and their numerous footnotes, the playing regulations and the rules of the International Cricket Conference. His advice was often sought on obscure matters of historical interpretation. If he had a weak spot, it was stubbornness.

He was convinced that the term 'Chinaman', as used in cricket, referred to the left-arm bowler's 'googly', or leg-break bowled with an off-break action out of the back of the hand. He had steadfastly maintained this position through a month's quite vituperative correspondence in the columns of *The Times*. Not one of a half-dozen letters could convince him that he was wrong.

'They've no proof, Peter,' he told Gauvinier. 'No proof.'

'Nor have you,' said Gauvinier reasonably.

'Ah, but I *know*,' said his friend, with such conviction that Gauvinier could have sworn he'd had it from the great W.G. himself. Now he just contented himself with, 'You'll see, one day you'll agree with me. Come on, drink up. We'd best be getting back to the ground.'

It was traditional courtesy for the home captain to be at the ground to greet the visiting team, although it was one which Gauvinier had found to be fading out in some quarters. So he had made a point of never arriving later than an hour before the start of play. The habit had an additional advantage in that it enabled him to deal with any last-minute emergencies that might arise.

'Mr Gauvinier, Mr Gauvinier.' Mrs Smith, hurrying breathlessly towards him, stumbled a little in her haste.

'What can I do for you, Mrs Smith? Nothing wrong with Norman, I hope?'

'No, not exactly. But he's out with the stable horse-box delivering a horse, and he's just phoned to say he won't be back before three o'clock. But he'll come quick as he can. He's terribly sorry.'

Gauvinier considered. If he won the toss, that would be all right. He wasn't going to bat last on such a day if he could help it, and young Smith was wanted for his bowling, not for his dubious ability with the bat. But if Raveley were to win the toss, they too would certainly choose to bat first, and that would pose problems. Norman Smith was the one bowler of real pace in the side, and without him the first half an hour could present Raveley with fifty or so easy runs. On the other hand, there wasn't another bowler in the village to be found, certainly not at the last minute.

'Never mind, Mrs Smith,' he said. 'I expect he'll go home to get his kit. Tell him not to get all hot and flustered, and we'll get by until he turns up. We can't afford for him not to play.'

'Oh, good. I'm so glad. He was so wanting to play and he was worried you'd put someone else in. Thank you, Mr Gauvinier, I'll tell him.'

With an effort, Gauvinier dismissed the problem from his mind. Time to worry about what to do when he had to. The Tillingfold players were beginning to arrive. Bill Budgeon, already changed into flannels, dismounted awkwardly from his one-pedalled cycle and stooped to unfasten his trouser clips.

'Afternoon, Bill. Feeling fit? You may have to open the bowling, you know. Norman's been held up. Hullo, James, hope you've brought some sixes in that bag of yours. Good afternoon, Mr Jess. Would you mind very much parking your car the other side of Mr Mitterman's? We always try to leave that space there for the visitors. Sorry to be a nuisance. How's that finger of yours?'

'No trouble, skipper. Just a bruise.'

By ten past two the pavilion was a-bustle with activity. Two or three of the team were changed into their whites and were knocking up on the outfield. Joe Deacon, happily clear-eyed, had donned his wicketkeeping gloves and had persuaded young White to throw him fast ones to warm his hands up.

Soon Mitterman came out with a bat to hit long high catches to the youngster, and they were joined by others.

Gauvinier just had time to worry if Raveley had mistaken the date (on one infamous occasion, after a former Tillingfold secretary had muddled his fixtures, each team had arrived at the other's ground) when a cheery cry announced 'coach's here'. He stepped across to shake hands with Troughton, Raveley's captain, whom he knew and liked from a dozen previous encounters.

'Hullo, Phil.'

'Nice to see you, Peter. Sorry we're a bit late. Couldn't get young Agnew here out of the pub.'

'That's good, it'll have taken some of the steam out of him, then.' Agnew was a swiftish bowler who'd taken four wickets last year. 'Let's toss as soon as you've got your whites on.'

But Troughton was the sort who wanted to get on with the game. Tossing presented him with no problems. He'd a strong team, which he knew would likely be too much for Tillingfold. He knew also that under Fanshawe's care the wicket would be a good one, and he wanted to give his batsmen some match practice out in the middle. 'Ten minutes out there's worth an hour in the nets' was a favourite maxim.

'Come on, let's toss now, before I change.'

So to the slightly bawdy encouragement of their respective teams, Gauvinier and Troughton walked chatting together to the wicket.

'Still got that old half-crown?'

'Of course.' Gauvinier had defiantly kept a King George V half-crown when the country had gone metric.

'Let's have a look at it. Can't trust you chaps not to put two heads on it.'

Gauvinier flipped it across. Troughton turned it this way and that, and flipped it back.

'Now that's what I call a coin,' he said. 'You toss, I don't need to look at Oliver's wicket today.'

'I bet you don't,' cried Gauvinier, laughing; and he spun the coin high in the air, glistening silver in the sunlight. Troughton called 'Heads!' as it reached its apex, and they let it fall on to the pitch between them. They both bent over it. Heads it was.

'Blast,' said Gauvinier, amiably. 'You'll be putting us in, then?'

'You bet I will. On second thoughts, it's too warm today for running about in the field. You'll have to get us out first.'

'Never you mind – we've got a secret weapon,' said Gauvinier, making fielding signs to his team. He wondered whether to say nothing, but decided Troughton was too old a hand to be bluffed. He needed eleven men in the field too badly.

'Phil, can you spare me a man for half an hour? One of our chaps has been held up.'

'Nothing easier. But you can't have our best cover point. Harry!' he called, 'Get your gear on and stand in as sub for a bit.' A young ginger-haired man with freckles grinned and came up to them.

'Harry Graves. This is Peter Gauvinier. D'you mind giving them a hand? He's no slouch, Peter.'

'Thanks, Phil, I'm sure he'll do us very nicely. It's only for a bit until one of our chaps turns up,' he explained, not saying, however, that it was Tillingfold's one fast bowler.

'Tea, at five. Draw stumps at seven-thirty as usual?' Tillingfold still kept to a time limit, not having adopted the modern idea of twenty more overs after six-thirty.

Fanshawe came up to him, wearing his white umpire's coat. 'Did you remember the tea urn, Peter?'

'Blast it, no.' Someone had to fill the electric urn with water and switch it on, or they'd get no tea. It was too heavy for the women to carry.

'I'll get Fred to do it. And we don't appear to have a scorer.'

'Thanks Oliver. Where's that young scallywag? Blast the boy. We'll have to ask one of the Raveley chaps to do it. A sub and a scorer.'

But he was spared the humiliation, as a bicycle swooped sharply off the road under the bumper of a passing car. A screech of brakes, an indignant blare on the horn and then a cloud of dust as the bike skidded sideways to a halt on the gravel gave way to an unrepentant grin set amid a thousand freckles.

'Garn, missed by a mile.' Bobby Bewers waved a V-sign after the car. 'Old twit can't see beyond his bonnet. Sorry, guv. Dinner was late today. Me mum threw the taters at me old man.' He grinned. 'She missed. Weren't arf a mess.'

'Righto, Bobby. Into your box with you. They're batting – I think the Raveley scorer's got their order already. We're one short, fielding a sub. Norman Smith's going to be late.'

'Oh, lor,' said Bobby, downcast, already halfway into the pavilion after his scorebook. 'What you goin' ter do?'

'You'll see.' He called into the pavilion door. 'All ready, blokes? Let's get on with it.'

Oliver Fanshawe, grave, grey-faced, and with a cream Panama hat and white boots to add to his white umpire's coat, accompanied the Raveley umpire, whom he knew well, to the wicket. 'Which end would you prefer, Mr Ryder?' Behind them Gauvinier, wearing his sky-blue Tillingfold cap, led out his team, the younger ones larking around, calling for the ball and eager for the fray, the more senior nearly as solemn as Fanshawe himself. They knew the problem facing Gauvinier, and each of them – critical as they often were of his captaincy – was secretly pleased he didn't have to cope with it.

Gauvinier had very little choice. His stock bowler, Budgeon, could be relied on to bowl tight and true, even with his disability, but he was by no means an opening bowler. Fred Bason could bowl tidy off-spin, but not with the new ball on a wicket as good as this one. He himself bowled slow left-arm, and on a wicket to suit him with his tail up, had been known to run through a side. But he'd never opened the bowling in his life, and knew too well his own early vulnerability. He'd never forgotten the day thirty years ago, when, in a trial match for the First XI, the school's champion high-jumper had hit him for five sixes in one over. It was a choice between Frank Hunter's vastly spun leg-breaks, Bason's more accurate finger-spin or his own flighted left-arm orthodoxy.

Gauvinier tossed the ball to Budgeon.

'It's up to you, Bill,' he said. 'We're going to have to bluff them into not scoring too many runs.'

'Aye, skipper. We'll do our best.'

Gauvinier sorted out his men. Convention demanded the substitute placed somewhere relatively innocuous. 'Third man, please, Ginger, opening from this end. Deep, right on the boundary, please.' Paul White was already in his position at cover. 'Gully, Frank,' he told Frank Hunter. 'Oh no, forgot your wrist. Better drop to mid-on, Frank. Edward, mid-off please, fairly deep, and drop to fine leg the other end. Colin – gully please, both ends.'

James Mitterman was stationed at square leg and Gauvinier, hoping the batsmen wouldn't take too much of a chance early on, brought Albert Jess up close at silly mid-on, with Fred Bason tucked in behind the batsman's hip pocket at leg slip.

In the meantime the Raveley opening batsmen had arrived, to a smattering of applause from the fieldsmen and some raucous encouragement from their colleagues from the pavilion. Both were old enemies. Ken Millington weighed all of fifteen stone, and his large moon face shone with pleasure at the day, the wicket, and the thought of caning his old rivals. He was a forcing bat, especially on the off side. His partner, no taller than Jess and just as slim, treated every ball as though it was encased in venom, and was the very devil himself to shift once he'd got his eye in. He rejoiced in the name of Albert Radnam, which spoonerism had turned into Bradman; so he was nicknamed 'Don'.

Radnam took strike. He could be relied on not to do anything rash in the first few overs and, from Gauvinier's point of view, his circumspection was an advantage. He was placing a great deal of faith on the arrival of Smith, a young and untried bowler. Tillingfold could be on a hiding to nothing.

Fanshawe stepped up to the wicket, casting an inquiring glance towards Radnam. 'Right arm over the wicket,' he called. The batsman straightened his bat, edge on to the umpire, and called 'Middle and leg, please, Mr Umpire.' Fanshawe motioned the bat towards the off. Radnam moved it slightly. The umpire's finger motioned again. Radnam gently kicked the toe of the bat away from him. Fanshawe's finger stopped. 'That is two legs, sir,' he said firmly. Holding his bat steady on the ground, Radnam stepped carefully behind it, marking the turf with the toe of his boot in best professional style, and then thumping his bat into the turf to make his blockhole. He glared suspiciously round the field and then settled into his stance at the wicket, left elbow well forward.

Fanshawe stepped back, glanced round to make sure every-one was ready, looked at his watch, folded his arms in front of him and called: 'Play!'

Chapter 4

Although Tillingfold had become accustomed to it over the years, Budgeon's shuffling, lurching gait to the wicket was an invariable source of amazement to visiting players and spectators. There is something almost embarrassing in seeing a cripple trying to play cricket like a normal healthy person, like watching an incompetent actor on stage. Batsmen playing against Budgeon for the first time felt somehow that Tillingfold were taking an unfair advantage: as if they were obliged not to hit the ball too hard, or expected to make allowances for the bowler's disability.

Neither of the Raveley openers were under any such illusions. Budgeon had made his place in the side through merit and keenness. Like many with incapacitated legs, he had developed tremendous strength in his arms and upper torso, and, although he could not bowl medium pace, he could induce surprising lift and pace off the pitch. His stock ball was a fraction short of a length, cutting back in at the batsman. He could bowl the leg cutter too, varying swerve and flight by the height of his arm at delivery. He was never a bowler to take liberties with.

Now Budgeon lurched in to the wicket, the smoothness of his arm action contrasting with the jerkiness of his legs. He delivered the ball high, on a good length and about a foot outside the off stump. Radnam lifted his bat and let it go through to the wicketkeeper. He had no need to play a stroke. Joe Deacon, standing back, took the ball firmly into his gloves and, feeling well on form, flipped it to Gauvinier to toss back. Gauvinier said quietly to him, 'Why don't you stand up? There's nothing wrong with this wicket and we might pressurize them a bit.'

Deacon, confident in his ability, shook his head. 'Not just yet. Let 'em get comfortable. We might surprise them.'

The next ball, straighter and faster, lifted a little. Radnam stepped back and across his wicket, in approved style, allowing the ball to hit the bat and drop in front of him. Jess moved in smartly and picked it up, throwing it to Mitterman at mid-on to pass on to the bowler when he reached his mark. Budgeon, knowing he'd a long afternoon ahead of him, turned and, shuffling in, delivered his third ball in exactly the same place as the second, meeting exactly the same response from Radnam. Budgeon knew he wouldn't tempt Radnam until he'd settled in, and concentrated on line and length, ball following ball to the end of the over with mechanical precision. Radnam met each ball with the full face of the bat, the last being driven quite firmly into the covers, where Paul White was only too glad to run in, field the ball with both hands and cut off a possible single.

'Hold it, Paul,' called Gauvinier, not wanting to risk any overthrows. 'Well bowled, Bill,' he shouted, and there was a smattering of applause for the end of a maiden over. Gauvinier made up his mind. If anyone had to be put into the firing line, it must be himself.

But as he set out his field, tossing the ball nervously from hand to hand, his mind could not dismiss the memory of those five sixes Charles Peake had hit off him twenty years ago. He wasn't helped by Radnam, who, for all his dourness as a batsman, was of a cheerful disposition. Leaning on his bat, satisfied that he had 'got his eye in' during the first over, he watched Gauvinier's dispositions with a knowing grin.

'You must be in trouble, skipper, putting yourself on so early.'

Gauvinier grinned. 'I'm our secret weapon. Been practising all winter.' But he knew he'd fooled nobody. Millington, the other Raveley batsman, took guard briskly, banging his bat down with 'thwacks' that could be heard all over the ground. He had made runs off Gauvinier's bowling before, and fancied his chances of a big score today.

Maybe he was over-confident. Gauvinier's first ball was slowish and pitched well up to him. He moved to drive, mis-hit completely, and sliced the ball off the outside edge just over the clutching fingers of Verrall in the gully. It wasn't a catch, but was near enough to one to jolt Millington out of his complacency, and to cause young Bobby in the scorebox to say to his opposite number, 'Another inch and that'd 've been a catch.' But the batsmen had gone through for two runs while Verrall retrieved the ball from behind him, glowering blackly at his bad luck.

Gauvinier asked the Raveley umpire to stand back from the wicket. He ran in to bowl, left arm round the wicket, at an angle of almost forty-five degrees, and he liked to cross the umpire's line of sight, not come in from behind him. He tried to deliver the next ball exactly the same as the first, for he felt, as most spin bowlers do who've been sliced over gully's head, that it was turn that had beaten the batsman.

This time he delivered a slow full toss, which Millington, stepping half forward, smashed past Mitterman at square leg for four. 'Right back to the boundary please, James,' called Gauvinier, trying to keep the irritation from his voice. He couldn't really blame Mitterman for not stopping a powerful pull off a bad ball, but he knew several other fielders on the side who would at least have tried. Now he sent down his best delivery – it floated slightly in from the off and straightened up, keeping slightly low. Millington, surprised, stabbed quickly down at it. It rapped him on the pads.

'Howzat!' Gauvinier's appeal split the heavens, and Deacon at wicket and Budgeon at slip both joined the appeal simultaneously. The Raveley umpire put his hand in his pocket, picked out a stone which he passed from one hand to the other, and said nothing.

Gauvinier bit back his annoyance. He never appealed unless he really believed the batsman was out. In his anger, he tried to deliver a faster ball, which turned into a long hop that Millington pulled, off the middle of the bat, for six. The Raveley players, lounging in the deck-chairs in front of the pavilion, clapped loudly. Bobby Bewers marked up his scorebook miserably and Groat, the Raveley scorer, with whom he didn't get on, leaned forward to call out, 'Ten up.'

The next ball was driven straight back, just on the off side. Gauvinier flung himself sideways, arm outstretched and just managed to get his fingers to the ball, half stopping it and diverting it towards the bowler's wicket. 'Get back,' shouted Millington furiously. Radnam, caught backing up, dived desperately for his crease as the ball hit the wicket to a concerted appeal from the entire Tillingfold side. The Raveley umpire backed off from the wicket and, stooping in concentration, shook his head as the ball cannoned away at an angle, catching the ginger-haired substitute off balance.

'Come on!' yelled Millington. Radnam picked himself up and ran a single as the substitute, Graves, seized the ball, and, anxious to prove he wasn't slacking, flung it wildly at the bowler's end. Gauvinier, stopping the ball on the half-volley, wide of the wicket, stung his hand for the second time but managed to prevent another run. He felt hot and flustered, as if an afternoon's cricket had happened in five balls.

Radnam faced the last of the over. He stopped it. 'Well bowled, skipper,' called young Trine. He was happy with the exhibition of hitting. He usually fielded in the deep, and there was always a chance of a good running catch with batsmen like Millington opening out. But thirteen runs were on the board and only two overs gone, thought Gauvinier, gazing towards the road and willing young Smith to appear.

Now Millington faced Budgeon, playing the first two balls confidently on the forward stroke, and then getting an inside edge past leg slip for two runs. Deacon tiptoed forward to take up his stance directly behind the wicket, hoping to catch Millington unawares. But the big man heard him coming and, stepping back from the wicket, he halted Budgeon in mid-shuffle with an outstretched hand.

'I'm too old a bird for that one.' He grinned at Deacon. He was feeling relaxed and easy now, the first tensions gone and he was getting the measure of the bowling. 'Play the game, Tillingfold,' came a slow cry from the pavilion, which annoyed the wicketkeeper.

Millington settled at the crease again watching Budgeon's halting run-up, the arm coming over high. It was a beautiful ball, drawing him forward on the front foot and cutting back off the pitch just sufficiently to beat the defensive stroke. Deacon moving across to the leg side with his body behind the ball in classic wicketkeeper's style, had the bails off in a flash, at the same time appealing triumphantly 'How's that!' As Millington was stretched right forward, the toe of his right boot still two inches outside the crease, the Raveley umpire's finger reluctantly travelled up towards his nose and then flicked forward. 'Out,' he said.

The whole side applauded a brilliant piece of leg-side stumping. Deacon, his every limb alight with pleasure, went up the pitch to Budgeon and clapped him on the back with his oversized gloves.

'What a ball, Bill. What a ball! He wasn't as fly as he reckoned he was.' And Gauvinier reflected, not for the first time, that a wicketkeeper can make all the difference to a team. If he's slack, or inefficient, then the whole fielding side tends to fall apart. If he's slick, and on his toes, it somehow lifts the performance of even the slowest fielder.

'Dammit, I knew he'd come up,' thought the burly Millington, taking off his batting gloves as he trudged back to the pavilion. 'Hard luck, Bert, just as you were nicely set, too,' called Troughton, and Millington, grinning at the memory of that pull for six, called back, 'I enjoyed that while it lasted.'

Bobby Bewers leaned out of his scorebox window and called, 'Fifteen, one, fifteen,' and a Raveley player, with much clanking, found the requisite numbers to put the score up on the board.

The next player, Spencer, was probably the most competent batsman on either side. He'd played several times for the county Second XI, and he had already scored more than five hundred runs for Raveley during the season. He took a brisk guard – 'leg stump, please' – and dealt confidently with Budgeon's first ball; a leg cutter this time, which he steered easily out to point for a single. 'Spencer likes to get himself off the mark with a single,' Groat said in the scorebox, more or less to himself. He didn't like scoring with a mere kid. He felt it was beneath his dignity.

'How's he doing this year?' With a wicket down, Bobby felt chatty.

'Two hundreds and a couple of fifties on top,' said Groat with pride, forgetting that he was one of the supporters of a move at Raveley to stop county players from being members of the Club.

'Garn. Don't say?' Bobby was so impressed that he forgot to watch the play, and missed a fine square cut from Radnam. Moving across, he had fairly thrashed the ball to the boundary past a startled Paul White. It was his first scoring stroke.

'Damn!' said Bill Budgeon under his breath. He'd let the ball go a little faster, looking for a touch outside the off stump; but it was short, and had invited such a stroke. He hadn't expected to see it played so fluently.

Fanshawe signalled the boundary, his right hand moving sideways, precisely and slowly. The Raveley scorer waved back his acknowledgement and leant out of the window. 'Twenty up.'

'Oh, that was a four, then?' asked Bobby, in surprise, giving Groat the pleasure of replying sharply, 'If you paid more attention, you'd score a bit better.' And Bobby, knowing he was right, was furious with himself and broke the lead of his pencil ticking off the numbers in his scorebook.

Fred Bason, crossing between the overs, stopped by Radnam to ask whether he'd kept that stroke in the cupboard and dusted it off specially for Tillingfold. And Radnam, leaning on his bat as if he'd made forty and not just four, told him that there were plenty more where that came from.

Gauvinier felt that tingle he always did when the teams warmed to the battle, and produced a beauty for Spencer. It pitched on the off stump, tight on a length, and broke sharply away. But Spencer, on the front foot, still had time to change his mind and late cut it beautifully wide of Budgeon's right hand. It was a stroke of real class, and at least three Tillingfold men applauded spontaneously. Paul White, fleet of foot though he was, could not stop it from crossing the third man boundary. 'Last time I saw that shot, it was Denis Compton at Lord's,' thought Bason appreciatively.

Without much conviction, Gauvinier moved White wider and right back to the boundary at deep point. On this form the youngster was going to have a lot of running to do. Spencer turned the next ball, pitched well up on the off stump, into a half-volley, and drove it streaking to the extra cover boundary, leaving both Trine and White helpless. Gauvinier, black memories crowding in on him, next tried to make one 'go with his arm' in towards the batsman's leg stump. Spencer, on one knee, clipped it stylishly just wide of square leg. Fielding well back, Mitterman had plenty of time to get behind the line of it. But he misjudged the strength of the hit, and the ball, hitting an uneven patch of grass, popped over his cupped hands and across the boundary for another four.

'Coo, three fours in a row,' said Bobby with envy. 'Thirty up,' he shouted to the Raveley batsmen lounging by the scoreboard. 'Thirty up.'

'Give us a chance, young 'un. He's scoring so fast we can't keep up,' someone called back, and Gauvinier felt a touch of resentment (mingled with admiration for its quality) that batting of such class should be unleashed on poor little Tillingfold. Fielders like Mitterman, he thought, would never be a match for batsmen like Spencer.

But his worst fears were not to be realized. He reverted to his stock ball, aimed at the off stump and turning away, and Spencer contented himself with a sober forward defensive prod. The fifth ball he drove hard and well wide of White at deep cover; but White, running flat out, scooped up the ball one-handed from the ground and flung it, flat and hard, right into Deacon's hands over the stumps. An almost certain four was turned into a sharp single, for Radnam had to hurry to beat the unexpected accuracy and speed of the throw.

The applause rang round the ground, and Gauvinier noticed that, as well as the Raveley batsmen lounging by the pavilion, some thirty or forty villagers had scattered themselves round the ground. Most of the benches under the trees were occupied, several youngsters were larking in the swings in the far corner, and there were three cars, attracted perhaps by the spectacle of white flannels on the rich green backcloth, or perhaps by Spencer's flurry of fours. He felt gratified by the youngster's keen piece of fielding.

'At least we're not folding up,' he said to himself, and was somehow inspired to make his next ball, the last of the over, spin really hard. The ball, turning and lifting sharply off a length, beat batsman, bat, wicket and wicketkeeper, and, darting past Budgeon's left hand at slip, rolled unchecked over the boundary for four byes. Deacon watched it go, hands on hips, the picture of misery.

'Never mind, Joe, it wasn't your fault,' called Gauvinier; but he knew that seventeen runs had come off the over, and that with only fifteen minutes gone Raveley had amassed nearly forty runs for the loss of only one wicket; and there was plenty of batting to come.

Bill Budgeon, shuffling and panting, the sweat sticking his shirt to his back, forced Spencer on to the defensive for five balls of the next over. To the sixth, perfectly straight, of perfect length, Spencer took one pace down the wicket and straight-drove it into the chestnut trees for six. Fanshawe turned slowly towards the scorebox and signalled, both hands raised above his head. It was suitable acclamation for a ruthless, clinical piece of execution. Budgeon swore to himself. He'd applauded the six as loudly as anyone, but he cursed the fact that that was the last ball of the over. He fancied his chances on top of a blow like that.

'Forty up.' Bobby Bewers went out to change the number himself – and to get a breath of fresh air. He found it difficult to put up with Groat's patronage; just as, no doubt, Groat could not bear the youngster's cheek, as he called it.

Gauvinier knew that had Spencer been facing the first ball of his over, his nerve would have broken and he would have taken himself off. After all, he'd conceded twenty-six runs in two overs. But with Radnam at the crease, Gauvinier felt he stood a chance of a wicket, and that at least he wouldn't get thrashed to all quarters of the ground.

As if to prove him wrong, Radnam stepped out to the first ball of the over and swept it so that one bounce carried it into the iron railings of the war memorial; and off the second ball brought up the fifty, with a delicate glance for three to long leg. Bason had a long chase and returned red-faced and panting. Spencer turned the next ball casually to square leg, and knowing the fielder, took two while Mitterman approached the ball, missed it, ran alongside it and finally wound himself up to loop it back to the keeper. Gauvinier ground his teeth and again tried his faster ball. It was short, well outside the off stump, and Spencer stepped back to give himself more room to thrash it through the covers. He hit it full in the meat, but slightly uppishly. Had it got to the boundary, it would have been a flat-hit six. But Paul White, with time only to take two paces before flinging himself far to his right, rolled over and came up holding the ball one-handed in the air. It was as brilliant a catch as any man on the field had ever seen, and Spencer, after dropping his bat in astonishment, ran over to congratulate the boy, with the whole fielding side in pursuit.

'Fifty-two, two, twenty-two,' called Groat hollowly, as the Raveley players rose to applaud Spencer, for his sportsmanship no less than his innings; while Gauvinier, and Bason, and Trine clustered round White. 'It just stuck,' he said in wonder, knowing that he'd remember this moment for the rest of his life. He couldn't recall the catch at all, just feeling the ball in his hand as he rolled over; but his right elbow was grass-burned, and his right knee and the side of his flannels were stained green where he'd flung himself along the ground. Gauvinier clapped him on the shoulder and told him, 'That was just what we needed, Paul. Marvellous catch.' And to cap the moment, Gauvinier saw, rounding the pavilion, the tall figure of Norman Smith. He waved him on to the field while the next batsman made his way to the crease, and trotted over to thank Graves for his assistance. Perhaps now the luck would turn Tillingfold's way. It wasn't before time, he felt.

Raveley's next man was long, lithe and very dark. He had high cheekbones and a silken moustache that drooped to a neat beard. His name was Mohinder, and he had come to Britain from Pakistan with his parents twelve years before. He took his guard with a quick tap of the bat, and hit Gauvinier's first ball straight back over the bowler's head for four. He tried to do the same with the next ball, but in fact accomplished a 'Chinese cut', the ball skidding off the inside edge of the bat away past fine leg for another four.

'They all look the same in the scorebook,' said Gauvinier, as the batsman apologized to him.

'Thank God you've arrived, Norman, they were about to slaughter us.

'Take a rest, Bill,' he called to Budgeon, 'then you can take my placc at this end.'

Chapter 5

In their praiseworthy efforts to abolish the slums of Britain's cities and at the same time to end the housing shortage which had bedevilled politics in the post-war period, the planners of the sixties and seventies embarked on a massive scheme to move people from the towns and to spread them around the countryside. 'Overspill' from the capital spread as far as Luton in the north and Brighton in the south. New conurbations were implanted upon the pleasant countryside, like Milton Keynes and Crawley New Town and Burgess Hill – acre upon acre of cheaply built flats and houses where woods and fields and streams and farms had existed before. And at the same time the planners decreed that acre upon acre of Victorian housing should be left to decay, while relics of historic chaos and confusion (like Covent Garden market) should be destroyed, and their place taken by concrete and plastic efficiency.

By the middle of the seventies, the planners were beginning to realize their mistake, discovering that in the place of the urban slums they so despised they had created thousands of square miles of urban dereliction; the communities they had split up and scattered had no wish (or could not afford) to return to work in the cities. Now the fear was that, with the heart removed from them, London and Liverpool and Manchester and Birmingham were slowly dying. To the urban slums and the suburban ribbon development had been added rural slums that sprawled across the countryside.

So now they began talking about reversing the trend, but it was too late to prevent the worst of the damage. Raveley, for example.

Until the Second World War, Raveley had been a village of

about half the size of Tillingfold; a village with a couple of pubs, a green, a cricket pitch, a church and a history. Now it was a series of brick and breeze-block estates, part houses, part flats, and a population of more than 100,000. The old village street had gone, to be replaced by concrete walkways and a modern shopping centre, flanked by those monuments to modern culture – Woolworths, Littlewoods, Marks and Spencer, Tesco, Boots, W. H. Smith, Sainsbury's, the Electricity Board, the Gas Board, Currys, chain store upon department store, trading stamps and cash offers.

Development had nearly put paid to Raveley Cricket Club. The first bulldozers had ripped up the village green, and Sainsbury's now stood where cricket had been played for a century and a half. For a couple of years Raveley CC carried on as 'Raveley Nomads', playing all their matches as away fixtures; but without a home of their own their spirit was rapidly flickering out. The club chairman, Ben Troughton, father of Philip, by patient pressure (he was a stubborn Sussex breed) eventually acquired from the Development Council the use of ground designated as 'open space', and cajoled his diminishing band of enthusiasts into building the club anew.

Soon the influx of new citizens began to have its effect. Most of them were ex-servicemen resettling, or skilled craftsmen come to work in the new factories springing up on the industrial estate. Although football was the passion of the majority, a significant proportion of the newcomers wanted to play cricket. The new field was rolled flat, levelled by bulldozer, and a square laid in record time. Sussex clay is a temperamental soil, but the one thing that can be guaranteed to grow on it is grass, and in no time at all Raveley were fielding first one, then two, and now three sides every Saturday. With a Thursday team, a colts team and two teams playing on Sundays, Raveley CC had become one of the largest amateur clubs in the south and soon would be challenging for the Haig National Cricket Club title itself. Ben Troughton, eighty-five and still attending home matches in his wheelchair, took pride in the fact that while his cricket club had become something of a power in the land, the soccer XI still languished in the lower reaches of the minor Sussex leagues, and the rugby club felt itself lucky if its First XV got a match with Horsham 'A'. In fact, it appeared that of the major traditional British sports, only cricket was really holding its own in Raveley. Club soccer and rugby in the mid-seventies seemed to reflect the national paucity of talent and interest; but there was a big upsurge in basketball, judo, karate, boxing, swimming, athletics and the other activities stimulated by the provision of a brand new sports centre.

The cosmopolitan nature of Raveley's population was naturally reflected in the composition of its sporting teams, and cricket was no exception. Mohinder, the new batsman, was one of a family of all-round sportsmen related to the famous Khans ('but who isn't, in Pakistan?' he had said modestly when introducing himself to Troughton). He'd missed a Cambridge Blue only through injury, and many pundits reckoned he was worth a county place. But he enjoyed club cricket for its own sake, while at the same time realizing that in this, as in his Austin Reed suits and silk scarves, he was only trying to be more English than the English. It was a trait common to many of his countrymen and one often misunderstood by the English themselves, forgetting that imitation is the sincerest form of flattery. He sold insurance as he played cricket and made love – with great enthusiasm, much skill and little self-control.

He was also one of four new citizens on the Raveley side. Tony Van den Berg, at number nine, was an electronics engineer, who had fled South Africa because he had been one of those rare Afrikaaners who violently opposed apartheid; while Aloysius Dewbury, the wicketkeeper, came from Jamaica. John Brewster was an Australian who'd come to Britain for three months in 1970, and who had stayed to play rugby in the winter, cricket in the summer, and to drive a minicab. He made a great deal of money and spent it on beer and sex and a holiday in the Mediterranean each year. The only thing he took seriously in life was sport, and he spent long hours and many pints of Foster's Lager loudly regretting he wasn't as fit as he should be.

None of the Raveley team had in fact batted against Norman Smith before, although two of them, the schoolboys Agnew and Graves, had played with him in the Billington School XI. His arrival, and the obvious relief it caused among the Tillingfold fielders, put the batsmen Radnam and Mohinder very much on their guard.

Norman paced out his run and asked Fanshawe for the marker. Budgeon didn't bother with such niceties, just scraped a line in the turf with his studs. Smith took a fifteen-pace run-up, curving in sharply towards the crease. But his action was high and easy, and he accelerated smoothly, pointing his left shoulder towards the batsman and lifting his left arm high, before bringing the right one over with a whiplash action that started at his waist and flowed smoothly through his arm and his wrist into his fingers. Nobody had taught him the action – it just came naturally, which meant that at sixteen he was indeed a bowler of rare promise.

He stood by Gauvinier as the skipper redeployed his fielders. Gauvinier had spent a considerable part of the past two summers watching first the Australians and then the West Indians, both in person and on the television. If there was one aspect of their play that had impressed him most, it was the spirit with which both teams fielded, and the aggressive way in which both captains, Chappell and Lloyd, set their field. He was also well aware that although Tillingfold had just taken a wicket, the psychological advantage, with sixty runs on the board in the first half hour of batting, was very much with the visitors. Now Smith had arrived, he hoped that he had the means of reversing the trend of a game which had threatened to run away from him.

So Norman was astonished to find himself bowling to a vastly more attacking field than he'd ever had at school. He had two slips (Gauvinier and Budgeon), and two gullys to go with them (Bason and Verrall). The only other fielder on the off side, patrolling a great arc from point to mid-off, was White, who stationed himself at what might be described as wide short extra cover. Jess, who'd looked pretty nippy although he hadn't had much to do in the field yet, remained at silly mid-on, with Hunter at short fine leg; and Mitterman, to his perturbation, found himself much too close (in his opinion) to the batsman at short backward square leg, three or four yards in front of the umpire; young Trine was left to patrol the rest of the outfield from wide mid-on.

Radnam, studying with interest both the umbrella of fielders behind him and Joe Deacon, standing a good ten yards back from the wicket, was impressed. 'Pretty quick, is he?' he asked Deacon, who, solemn-faced, nodded and took a calculated couple of paces further back. As soon as Radnam turned to take fresh guard from the umpire Deacon grinned, eased forward three paces and sank on to his haunches, waiting for the delivery. Radnam, however, was not easily intimidated. He was Raveley's regular opener, and he was used to coping with some pretty lively bowling.

Cricket captains, like God, propose; and man, in the form of bowler and fielders, dispose; and Gauvinier's good intentions had failed to take full account of the fact that he was asking a great deal of a sixteen-year-old boy. As he ran up to bowl his first ball, Norman forgot the umbrella of close catchers waiting behind the line of the wickets, and remembered only the wide open spaces to his left and right. In consequence the ball, though fast, was a straight full toss, and was met firmly by Radnam and driven back past him for four runs.

'Faster they bowl, faster they go to the boundary.'

Young Bobby thought he'd heard quite enough from Mr Groat. 'You wait and see,' he said ominously, aware it wasn't much of a retort.

The second ball was better – on a length and straight at the leg stump. Radnam, playing back,was beaten for speed, and the ball rapped him high on the thigh. Deacon, from behind the wicket, appealed for leg before wicket, but Norman, apart from a hopeful look at the umpire, did not. Mr Fanshawe was unmoved and Radnam, hobbling away and rubbing his thigh vigorously, muttered, 'Some people'll appeal for anything,' although in truth the ball was not that far off the wicket.

Norman, settling down into his rhythm, bowled a really good ball just outside the off stump. It appeared to swing slightly away and lift off the pitch. Radnam stabbed at it and was fortunate not to get a touch, and the ball smacked into

Deacon's gloves at chest height, even though he was standing well back.

'That's better,' said Bobby in the scorebox. 'He was jolly unlucky there.'

'What d'you mean, unlucky? Don pulled his bat away from that one.'

'Not likely, he hadn't a clue.'

'Watch the game then.'

The fourth ball of the over flicked off Radnam's pads and was well taken low and to his right by Bason.

'How's that!' called a spectator on the boundary; the players' tension was infectious.

'Crowd catch,' mumbled Groat in a temper. Suddenly the game was in earnest. The last two balls of the over beat Radnam completely, both leaving the bat and moving just too far for him to get a touch. He was relieved to hear Fanshawe call 'Over', and he took off his cap and wiped his brow on the back of his arm. 'Hot out here,' he said to nobody in particular. Gauvinier, highly pleased with Smith's arrival and his first over, ran up to him and whispered a few instructions in his ear. 'I'll try, guv,' said Norman eagerly. 'Next over.'

Bill Budgeon, thankful for an over's rest in the slips, took Gauvinier's place at the far end. He didn't mind which end he bowled, or even whether he bowled at all. He was content just to be in the game. He liked the way Gauvinier had applied the pressure on the Raveley batsmen, and he was determined to follow it up. He asked Gauvinier to reinforce the off-side field.

It was one of Budgeon's theories, which he often expounded to his friend Colin Verrall, that a bowler could get as much benefit by playing on a batsman's strength as he would trying to exploit his weaknesses. Now he moved White back to deep point on the boundary, Verrall wider and closer, in the gully. Jess he brought over to short extra cover and he waved back Trine to deep mid-off. With Norman Smith at forty-five degrees from the wicket and Gauvinier at slip, Budgeon had six men on the off side. He knew Mohinder for a spectacular, wristy batsman, who particularly favoured the square cut and the off drive; and with the field set to his liking he concentrated on keeping the ball on a length, on the line of the off stump. He didn't bother about swerve, or cut, or spin – just held the ball with his first two fingers along the line of the seam and let the pitch do the rest.

The first ball was slightly overpitched. Mohinder, left foot down the pitch and well across to the line of the ball, drove it sweetly enough, but not quite timed, hard to Jess's right. Jess, half stooping, half diving, fell on it and fielded like a goalkeeper, clutching the ball two-handed to his chest. The batsmen, after some 'yes' – 'no' – 'wait' calls to each other, decided not to run at all, and there was a smattering of applause. Behind the boundary, leaning on the iron railing separating the chestnut trees from the road, Harry Broome turned to a couple who'd left their car to watch. 'Pretty smart fielding side, Tillingfold,' he said with pride.

'Gee, that looked good. But we don't know a thing about it,' said the man, in a Texas drawl. 'So this is cricket? Can you tell us how you play it?' And the amiable Broome launched into the pleasurable but exasperating task of explaining the intricacies of a game which he, like so many Englishmen, seemed to have in his blood although he himself had never bowled a ball or waved a bat in earnest.

Budgeon delivered a similar ball. This time Mohinder, timing it better, placed it beyond the reach of Jess, and young Trine, running hard to his left, picked up the ball cleanly and jerked it back to the wicketkeeper. It was a competent enough throw on the first bounce, but it couldn't prevent the batsmen going through for two runs. The next ball was shorter, slightly faster, and Mohinder, well up on his toes with his right foot across the wicket, executed the perfect square cut with a flourish of the wrists. Off the meat of the bat, the ball flashed under Verrall's sudden grab and, neatly bisecting White and Smith, raced over the boundary for four.

'Seventy up,' called the Raveley scorer, and Millington and Spencer both wished they hadn't got themselves out (for that's how they felt about it): for with such bowling as this it appeared the lucky batsman could score at will.

Bill Budgeon went back to his mark, rubbing one side of the

ball hard along the front of his right thigh, having first moistened it with sweat from his forehead. As he turned at his mark, he fitted it into his hand, the shiny side towards the off and the seam of the ball slanting down towards the batsman's pads, slightly across his fingers. He delivered it from the full height of his arm, his biceps brushing his ear, and he brought his arm over and down as fast as he could, with a whip of the wrist.

The ball, as he'd hoped, was faster than normal. It pitched almost exactly where the previous one had, outside the off stump and just short of a length. But this time the angle of the seam, the height of the delivery arm and the added speed meant that it swerved slightly in the air and cut back a little off the pitch towards the batsman. Mohinder, back and across the wicket to repeat the previous successful four, found the ball coming faster and closer to him than expected. Already committed to the stroke, he hit it well enough, but this time it flew from the middle of the bat at waist height straight to Verrall in the gully. Verrall, unmoving, took the ball in front of his ample stomach and, being something of a humorist at times, slipped it into his trouser pocket all in the same movement; then, swinging round, he shaded his eyes with one hand and gazed towards the boundary. Mohinder, half fooled into thinking the ball had gone through the fielder's hands, checked his instinctive stride towards the pavilion and, as the laughter rippled round the field, grinned in exasperation and continued his walk.

On the boundary, Harry Broome explained to the Americans, 'He was bowling for that one. See, he pitched that ball a yard shorter than the last ...' without relieving their ignorance in any way whatsoever. Indeed, it was doubtful that more than a half a dozen men on the ground could appreciate the real subtleties of that ball, or the imagination and the skill that went into its delivery. The catch, however, was obvious enough, and the fielders clustered round Verrall, excitedly congratulating him.

' 'Twere nowt,' he said modestly. 'Had to 'old 'un or I'd 'a lost my manhood.' And Bill Budgeon, happy to have taken his second wicket without too many runs being hit off him, bantered, 'No chance of that, Colin, not with them bloody great hands of yours. Like paddles they are.'

And then they turned, and went back to their places in the field, as Gauvinier called 'Man in' and led the obligatory applause for Phil Troughton, the opposing captain. With seventy on the board and only three men out, there was still a great deal for Tillingfold to do. Troughton, a cool, competent player, was both an old friend and an old enemy, who met his first ball with a professional turn of the wrist which sent it speeding towards Mitterman at square leg.

'Yes,' called Radnam, starting down the pitch from the bowler's end. Troughton, who hadn't yet acclimatized himself to the field, called back 'No, wait', and paused, watching the ball. It shot through Mitterman's hands, cracked him hard on the shins and rebounded fast towards Bason at short fine leg. Seeing the misfield, Troughton called 'All right, come on.'

Radnam, flustered, turned to run again, saw Bason pick up the ball and called 'No.' But by this time Troughton was well down the pitch and going hard. Radnam, unable to send his captain back, did the best to make the run after all. But Bason was an old hand, and he tossed the ball accurately and unhurriedly back to Deacon. The wicketkeeper had all the time in the world to remove the bails without any fuss and to appeal, with Radnam already walking angrily towards the pavilion. Troughton was appalled. 'So sorry, Don. So sorry,' he called. 'All my fault.' To which Radnam replied with a grunt and, striding into the pavilion, threw his bat across the room.

'Proper case of yes, no, sorry,' said Trine cheerfully to Budgeon. 'That's much better.'

Bobby Bewers called out 'Seventy, four, fifteen', while Harry Broome found himself with a whole new situation to describe to his American friends.

'Gee, I always thought cricket was a slow game. This beats baseball any day,' said the attractive wife: and Broome hastened to explain that this was only village cricket. If the visitors wished to see the real thing, they'd have to visit Lord's or the Oval, or perhaps Hove next week, when Sussex were playing at home. 'Or you might always watch a Test match on television,' he advised, thereby mystifying them even further.

In the meantime, Mitterman, almost oblivious to the fact that he'd been at least partly instrumental in the fall of the last wicket, was down on one knee rubbing his shin. Already he could feel a large lump developing, and his leg felt heavy and painful when he put his weight on it. He wasn't much comforted by Gauvinier's dry, 'Well fielded, James. It always pays to get your body behind the ball', or by Fred Bason's cheery, 'We'll have to join Billington United, you and me. With that sort of combination we'll be unbeatable.' He limped heavily back to square leg as the next man in, Brewster, the Australian, faced up to the last ball of the over. He played back to it and missed; for once Deacon got his gloves tangled up, and let through the ball for two byes.

Both Gauvinier and Troughton, the opposing captains, felt that the crisis of the innings had now been reached. Gauvinier, with four good batsmen out, was conscious that seventy runs in forty-five minutes was a pretty good start, and that he needed to limit Raveley's score to under one hundred and twenty if he was to give his own rather shaky batting a chance of success. But he was delighted with the success of his tactics and with the team's fielding, and he felt well on top of the Raveley batsmen.

Troughton, although angry with himself over the mix-up that had led to Radnam's dismissal, was too good a cricketer to brood on the incident. He knew that a good steady innings was needed, to brace the side after a heady start had been rather thrown away, and he took guard firmly, deciding to apply himself to the task. He was a safe, rather than a spectacular batsman, but he had made some good scores against Tillingfold in the past, and he was not inclined to underestimate the fielding side's ability. He knew only too well the unpredictability of cricket; and the fact that he was forty years old, while the bowler was a mere sixteen (or that he was a respected solicitor and Norman Smith a stable lad), would make not a jot of difference to what was written in the scorebook.

Smith, no matter how young he was, had also realized the significance of the moment, and he determined to do his best to follow his captain's instructions. 'Try to bowl at the off-stump, Norman, first five balls inswingers. Then give him an out-swinger if you can.' Gauvinier had once seen the England fast bowler, Geoff 'Horse' Arnold, dismiss New Zealand's record-breaking opening batsman Glenn Turner this way at Lord's. He knew it was a tall order to ask a youngster to bowl as accurately as that, but he was also aware that some direction for a young man was better than no direction at all, so he made the suggestion and hoped.

Smith, running in to bowl, felt a surge of confidence. He lengthened his stride, leapt smoothly at the crease and hurled his arm over. It was an inswinger all right – a beauty. It swung from outside the off stump, pitched on a length and nipped 'through the gate' between bat and pad amid a loud roar, clipping the top of Troughton's leg stump and sending the bails flying over Deacon's head. Smith, with the rest of the Tillingfold side, leapt in the air, arms uplifted in triumph, only to be deflated on seeing Troughton recover his balance, turn and begin to mend the wicket, instead of heading for the pavilion. He looked round at Fanshawe. The umpire was signalling towards the scorebox. 'No-ball,' he called, and Norman realized that the roar he'd heard as the ball hit the stumps was not his own shout of pleasure but the umpire's call. Fanshawe walked to the popping-crease and pointed his toe, indicating where Smith had gone over the line. Gauvinier called, 'Hard luck, Norm. Let's have another one there.'

It said a great deal for Smith that he did not allow the misfortune to throw him off balance. Bowling more carefully, he delivered the rest of the over to order. Five balls went down, each of them swinging in to the batsman. Three of them Troughton was able to leave alone, as they swung across his body and down the leg side, making Deacon leap and stretch to stop them from going for byes. True, Troughton played carefully, once going right up on his toes to bring the ball down on to the pitch in front of him with the straightest of bats, dropping his wrists and slackening the fingers round the bat handle. The seventh, aimed straight at the middle stump, had Troughton driving across the line trying to work it away to mid-wicket. It moved off the pitch again, but this time in the other direction, touching the outside edge of the bat as it went and winging its way chest high to Gauvinier at first slip – a straightforward, finger-tingling slip catch. He flung the ball high in delight – for himself, for Norman, for the ball, for the catch, for the score and for the sheer joy of cricket.

Amid the general applause and excitement that ran round the ground at the fall of the wicket, the Raveley scorer's voice rang like the knell of doom. 'Seventy-three, five, nought.' Bobby Bewers went round to find and put up the 'duck' in place of the 'o'. Troughton was one of those who had earned the honour. 'It's amazing, this game,' said Trine, amiably, to Mitterman. 'Ten minutes ago they were seventy for two. Now they're seventy-three for five – three runs and three wickets.'

Mitterman, still smarting from the blow on his shin, agreed gloomily. 'But there's a long way to go yet,' he said. 'Raveley always produce a dark horse or two.'

Trine glanced at him sharply, but Mitterman seemed not to have noticed. In fact the new batsman, Dewbury, bore a strong resemblance to the West Indian captain, Clive Lloyd. He was black, tall and shambling, carrying his bat out to the wicket in his left hand as if it were a club. Like Lloyd, he batted left-handed in a loose-limbed free-hitting style, and bowled right-handed. He also kept wicket if asked, scuttling back and forth behind the wicket like a long-legged spider, ungainly but effective. He was a gentle soul, who drove a lorry for the Raveley hospital where his wife was a nursing sister. He grinned as he passed Trine.

'I may be a dark hoss, but I sho' try to kick like a mule, boss,' he said in his deep voice.

'Good for you,' said Trine heartily, blushing for his friends and running back to his position in the outfield. He was distracted by the sight of two girls ducking under the railing and spreading out a rug on the grass under the trees. From this distance, they both looked young and pretty. One was blonde, the other brunette, and Trine noticed they were both wearing skirts. It wasn't that he objected to well-fitting jeans, he said to himself. But skirts were so much more interesting if you were fielding in the deep. Cricket took on an added dimension when there was a spot of talent around. Trine edged along the boundary to get a better view. He was startled into attention by a stentorian shout from the field.

'Catch it, Trine.'

'Catch what?' thought Trine, gazing desperately around in the air. At the last second he saw the ball, lofted high into the air by Brewster, flying towards the boundary to his right. He lunged, and in fact did well to get a hand to it. The ball hit the top joint of his fourth finger and bounced unchecked over the boundary line, where it smacked against a tree trunk and rolled between the two girls. They shied, giggling, out of its way.

'Sorry!' called Trine, instantly miserable. He'd dropped a catch which, if he'd been paying attention, would have been relatively easy; and he'd spoiled Bill's average at the same time. The girls certainly wouldn't give such a rotten fielder another glance, and he hated making a fool of himself in front of an audience. There must have been a hundred people round the ground by now, with twenty or thirty cars lining the road, under the spread of the chestnut trees and round the corner to the war memorial. Among the spectators in the deck-chairs over by the pavilion Trine saw his parents. His father, red-faced, leant towards his wife, who was leaning back and looking up to the sky, and did something. Even at this distance Trine could see he was laughing. His mother's head assumed an annoyed angle. Trine's finger hurt.

Trine tossed the ball back underarm and resolved not to be distracted again. Brewster, who favoured the 'swipe', described by the *Oxford English Dictionary* as 'a blow at the full stretch of the arms; particularly in cricket', pulled Budgeon's next ball hard along the ground, and Trine, rushing at it too fast, half stopped it and was forced to double back in his tracks to prevent it going for four; meanwhile the batsmen ran three and the Raveley scorer remarked to Bobby, 'You're side's getting rattled, then.' And raised his voice again to call 'Eighty up.'

There was a pause in the proceedings while the left-handed Jamaican took guard and the field adjusted itself. Budgeon was never so happy bowling to a left-hander as he was to an orthodox right-handed batsman, and consequently tried to bowl too carefully. The result was a straight full toss which Dewbury struck back past him for four – a tremendously powerful stroke, all along the ground.

Budgeon tried to 'tweak' one with his powerful fingers, but it too was overpitched, and Dewbury pulled it, on the full toss, to the square leg boundary. But White was there and, as so often, a good stroke which had deserved four was well stopped, and the batsman had to be content with one.

Budgeon polished the ball very carefully before bowling. Fourteen runs had come off his first four balls. He turned and examined Brewster, who was almost square on, balancing on his back foot, flexing his knees and tapping his bat at the same time. It was the stance of a hitter. Budgeon gave him a perfect ball, straight and on a length. Brewster took one pace down the pitch and hit it clean out of the ground over Trine's head. The ball sailed clear of the chestnut trees, pitched on the far side of the road and bounced into the centre of the muddy pond. Once more the applause rippled round the field and Budgeon, standing watching the ball's flight as it disappeared over the chestnut trees, said appreciatively, 'That was some hit.'

Brewster, thrilled at the applause but even more so at the feel of the ball as it left his bat, leaned on the handle and watched the antics of the village schoolboys as they tried to fish the ball out of the muddy pond. Umpire Fanshawe walked with measured step to the pavilion, with ironical cheers from the Raveley players breaking out around him, and emerged with a partly-used ball which he threw to the Raveley umpire for inspection. He passed it on to Budgeon.

Budgeon, vengeance in his heart, sent down the last ball of the over – a slower ball this time, an innocent half-volley, just asking for the same treatment. Brewster leapt out at it, swung mightily – and missed. The ball carried on its gentle course and discreetly clipped the middle stump. The two bails fell off quietly, and lay together with the ball at the foot of the stumps like a sort of cricketing still life. Brewster glared at the offending sight and then at Joe Deacon behind the stumps, as if he suspected the wicketkeeper of some dark plot, and at last departed, muttering to himself in wonder at missing a simple half-volley. Quite a number of people on the ground could have told him that the batsman who will cart a good length ball to the boundary will just as easily hit across a half-volley and be bowled.

'Lumme,' said Bobby Bewers in awe, 'that must have turned a foot.'

'Never.' Groat, for all his superiority of demeanour, had seen a great deal of cricket in his time and knew good bowling when he saw it. 'Didn't move an inch. He set Johnny up for it beautifully – tempted him with that six and then – whap!'

'D' you reckon so?' said Bobby. 'I'll ask Bill at tea.'

Agnew, Raveley's eighth batsman, was at the crease, and the field had changed over. Norman Smith was getting ready to bowl. Gauvinier stopped him with a raised hand and, turning in the direction of the scoreboard, bellowed 'Telegraph!'

Groat waved acknowledgement and apology at the same time. When and how 'telegraph' had come to mean that the scoreboard was not keeping pace with the play lay in the mists of the past. In the excitement of Budgeon's over both scorers had forgotten not only the wicket but also to keep the 'tens' going up on the board.

'Ninety-three, six, fifteen,' called Groat, and one of the Raveley batsmen obliged.

Norman Smith, with two overs and a wicket under his belt, was fully into his rhythm by now, and bowled a beautiful over to Dewbury, fast and hard, the ball fizzing through off a length and making the batsman play at each one. Dewbury, subdued, was forced to use all his experience to keep the ball out of his wicket. He was relieved, too, when the last ball of the over caught a thick edge and flew, fortunately for him, wide of the slips down to third man for two runs.

'Thank you, Bill, well bowled,' called Gauvinier to Budgeon. Even though the shoemaker had taken a wicket with the last ball of his previous over, he had conceded nineteen runs, and it looked as though the heat was taking a toll of his stamina.

'OK, boss,' Budgeon called back. 'Time I took a rest anyway.' And he shuffled happily into the slips, his permanent position when he wasn't bowling. Gauvinier looked around and tossed the ball to Frank Hunter.

'See what the wicket'll do for you, Frank. I've an idea it'll turn plenty.' And Frank Hunter, who during Budgeon's expensive last over had been itching to get his hands on the ball, flushed with pleasure at being chosen before his old friend and rival, Fred Bason.

Chapter 6

Gauvinier tried to deal with the perennial squabble between Hunter and Bason, or 'Frank 'n' Fred' as the village called them, by ignoring it, which sometimes worked. But he knew himself to be affected and irritated by it. Frank was potentially the better cricketer. He had a natural eye for ball games, batted and bowled with considerable unorthodox flair and total inconsistency, and had very quick reactions in close fielding positions. Much of his time he spent warring with the rest of the world, either collectively or individually; and when he'd run out of targets for his ill-temper, he turned it equally easily on to himself. He ran Tillingfold's largest garage with a fine attention to mechanical excellence and a compensating disregard for business efficiency, which meant he was always busy and always broke.

Fred Bason the builder, on the other hand, was of more solid stock. He'd waited patiently for his father to pass away; waited patiently for his business to grow; waited patiently for his cautious investments to mature; and he was quite prepared to bowl or bat all afternoon. His off-breaks turned occasionally, and minimally; his broad bat could assume, to the unfortunate bowler, the proportions of a barn door; and his gentle smile hardly changed at all. Only on a day like this, with the sun feeling hotter as every minute passed, his red face grew redder and redder, his shirt stuck to his wide back, and his trousers stretched across his wider backside as he crouched at leg slip.

In their youth Frank 'n' Fred had been inseparable, Fred's easygoing nature compensating for Frank's more mercurial flashes of temperament. But eighteen years ago, when Fred was twenty-four, he'd gone to collect his sweetheart and fiancée, Rosie Verrall, to take her to the pictures. He'd been met at the door by her brother Colin, with a small box and an envelope. In the box was the single stone engagement ring he'd bought Rosie in Billington six months before; in the envelope was a note. 'I don't know how to say this, but I can't go through with it. It's not your fault; I'm going to marry Frank. I'm so sorry, darling. Thank you for everything.'

So Fred had placed the note in the box with the ring, thanked Colin gravely, and gone home, where he put the box carefully away in a drawer. He'd even agreed to be Frank and Rosie's best man, standing there solid and square in his hired morning suit and smiling his quiet smile. He had toasted the bride and groom at the reception afterwards, in the big room at the rear of 'The Dog and Duck', ending his speech with the words, 'They say, let the best man win. Well, I'm the Best Man today and I didn't win. Or did I?' The guests had laughed and applauded, but Frank had shot him a look. Since then things hadn't been quite the same. Rosie had grown shrill, burdened with four children, and Frank, struggling against mounting debts, was becoming impossible to live with; while Fred had never married but had built a good business and amassed a comfortable fortune.

Gauvinier's current problem was that he knew that Frank Hunter was the bowler who was more likely to take a wicket; but that Fred Bason would be more liable to keep the scoring rate down. Once more the match was teetering in the balance. With roughly an hour and a quarter before tea, Raveley could place the match beyond Tillingfold's reach. It had taken only just over an hour to score ninety-three runs. The bowlers and the fielders were getting jaded, if not tired. The Raveley batsmen, particularly Dewbury and Agnew, the pair in now, could well double the score before declaring.

On the other hand, if Tillingfold could break through, with Smith still on top form, they might even have Raveley on the run in an over or two. If ... Gauvinier decided to take the gamble with Hunter.

Frank Hunter had a curious delivery. He bowled orthodox right-arm leg spin with the occasional googly, spinning the ball by twisting his wrist and producing it from the back of his hand. But he did it after the style of the late great Doug Wright of Kent – off the wrong foot and with a windmill twirl of the arms. In consequence, the ball was delivered much faster than it was by the usual leg-spinner's method off the front foot. When Frank was in form on a hard and dusting wicket, he was virtually unplayable. But, like the little girl, when he was bad, he was 'orrid.

Agnew, the young fast bowler, was also a useful number eight for Raveley. Actually he opened the batting and the bowling for his school. But he had never met an action like Hunter's before, and was taken completely by surprise. The first ball was not a leg break – Hunter liked to bowl a fast top-spinner or two to get his length, before trying to spin the ball. This one, delivered off the wrong foot and therefore before Agnes was expecting it, leapt off the pitch and reared straight at the young man's face. He flung up his bat involuntarily to protect himself and the ball caught his shoulder, flicking high over Bason's head at gulley and down, on the bounce, to Trine at third man. One run. Hunter grumbled to himself, going back to his mark. 'The old bugger didn't even try for it.'

Dewbury, the left-hander, knew Hunter's action well, and was ready for anything. But he didn't expect a nasty shooter, to which he just got his bat down in time and 'dug out' towards mid-wicket, where Mitterman's finickety fielding permitted another single.

Hunter's third ball once again had Agnew all at sea. It was a fast leg break, pitching on middle stump and whipping away outside the off stump, leaving the batsman groping. Deacon took it slickly and removed the bails, but did not appeal. Hunter threw up his arms in frustration and glared at the wicket. His fourth ball was another beauty. The young batsman, desperate, tried to drive. But this ball, like the last, moved away from the swing of the bat and flew off the outside edge to Bason, who took it low and to his left with both hands, safely this time.

'Well taken, sir,' cried Gauvinier, running up to clap Fred on the back. 'That young man can be a very dangerous bat.' Bason, pleased at taking a stiff one on his left side, jerked the ball back to Hunter. 'Sorry I couldn't reach the first one, Frank,' he called, and Hunter, elated at the wicket and at his own form, called back, 'You'd have needed elastic arms for that one, Fred,' without forgetting to add, to himself, '... if you'd tried for it.'

'Ninety-six, seven, one,' called Bobby, his voice breaking with excitement. 'Only three to go and not yet a hundred.'

'Don't you worry, we're not finished yet, by a long chalk,' Groat immediately admonished him. It appeared the Raveley scorer was right, as Van den Berg, the new batsman, swung Hunter's next ball, an atrocious full-toss, round to leg for four runs.

'One hundred up,' he called out; the applause for the boundary swelled around the ground, and the players joined with the spectators in clapping as the magic figure went up on the scoreboard.

Hunter, annoyed with himself for the full toss, set his teeth and tried his fastest leg-break. It pitched short, a rank long hop, and would have flown a yard wide of the off stump had not Van den Berg slashed wildly at it. The ball flew and looped down fearfully fast to third man. There Trine, all attention now, had time to look down and adjust his feet inside the boundary line before he took the catch in both hands at his right shoulder, swaying but not stepping back over the line.

Van den Berg departed, slapping his bat angrily against his pad as he made his way back to the pavilion, while the bowler, almost persuading himself that it was all his doing, forced himself to say to Verrall, who was the nearest fielder, 'It's amazing the way a bad ball will get a wicket when the good ones don't.'

Dewbury went to meet the new man in, the other schoolboy, Graves. 'Try and let me take the bowling, man, if you can.'

But when Dewbury hit the first ball of Smith's next over firmly to mid-wicket, Graves allowed his youthful exuberance to get the better of him and went for the run without hearing Dewbury's call of 'wait'. Dewbury, shrugging his shoulders, sauntered up the pitch for a comfortable single. 'Run up!' someone shouted from the boundary.

'Silly ass,' said Troughton to Spencer. 'He's given it away.'

'Oh, I don't know, we want all the runs we can get,' came the reply.

'But not at the risk of a wicket at this moment. Oh, no ... look at that! What did I tell you?'

Smith's next ball, a fast straight yorker, had crashed through Graves's guard, spreadeagling the wicket and leaving the stumps at all angles.

'A hundred and three, nine, nought,' the two called together, and the Raveley captain intercepted his last man on the way to the wicket.

'Try and keep your end up, Andy. Straight bat and leave it all to Aloysius.'

'Righto, skipper. I'll try.'

Andy Boggs was short, balding and fifty; but his stocky body carried not one ounce of fat. He ran the keep-fit classes, the judo training and the karate at the Raveley sports centre; and managed a flourishing physiotherapy clinic of his own. Apart from Smith, possibly, and the youngsters Agnew and Graves, he was certainly the fittest man on either side. But, as he was the first to admit, although his body was a magnificently trained and beautifully coordinated machine, when it came to managing a bat or a ball he lacked the one essential – timing. He was selected by Raveley for games like this one because of his immense enthusiasm and willingness to take part in anything, and because he cheerfully stood in as twelfth man, or umpire, or even scorer, if they could find no one else. He also paid the subscriptions regularly.

He took guard and decided to use the prod to the first ball, no matter what. He had two strokes – a forward prod and a backward poke. He took his stance at the wicket with his left wrist uncomfortably bent round the handle of his bat, and with a good six inches of handle showing between each glove. His feet were placed far back from the blockhole, so that his body bent over towards the bat, totally inhibiting him from swinging it even if he wanted to. His forward prod was made simply by moving bat, front pad and body forward a pace without varying his stance. The backward poke was made by reversing the process – taking one pace backward but then poking vaguely in the direction of the ball. He had a third alternative when he was not sure which to do – he kept his bat in the blockhole and moved neither limb nor muscle.

He had four balls to face in the over. The first he met with his forward prod, as he'd already decided. The ball struck the face of the bat and rolled up the pitch. A smattering of applause came from the Raveley men in the pavilion, thankful even for a show of resolution. To the second he played his backward poke, scooping the ball away from his wicket with the bottom of his bat a fraction before it hit the stumps. He knocked it clear, and Norman let out a strangled squeak of frustration which might just have been an appeal. 'Not out,' said Oliver Fanshawe; and the Raveley players, who thought the appeal had been for an obscure offence – 'hitting the ball twice' – called out angrily, 'Play the game, Tillingfold.'

Norman, unsettled by the unexpected barracking, sent down his fastest outswinger, and Boggs, prodding forward, edged it to slip where Budgeon put down a fairly straightforward chance, the ball stinging the tips of his fingers and carrying on straight through his hands for two runs.

'Sorry, Norm,' he called. 'I were gathering day-dreams.' Which was his way of concealing the fact that his crippled leg was hurting like hell.

Andy Boggs, pleased to be let off and to have opened his score, grinned cheerfully and took the next ball, a fast lifting inswinger, on the left thigh without wincing. The ball, catching Fred Bason unawares at leg slip, flew out of his hurried left-handed grab and went down to long leg for another two – this time signalled as leg byes by Fanshawe.

'Now,' Spencer lit a cigarette and blew out the first mouthful of smoke. 'Let's see what the poor man's Clive Lloyd can do.'

Frank Hunter, still elated at getting two wickets in one over, regarded any batsman as his natural prey. In his overconfidence he delivered a full toss well up and on Dewbury's legs. Dewbury, choosing his place and his timing, clipped him sweetly past square leg for four runs. The third ball he drove through the off field for another four, and then, treating a long hop to his left-hander's pull, hit a huge six off the fifth ball.

'Hundred and twenty up.'

Dewbury casually cut the last ball of the over fine and, forcing the willing Boggs to run hard, took three to 'farm' the bowling.

'Keep it up, Aloysius.' Troughton's voice, glowing with pleasure, came from the pavilion as the fielders changed over. Dewbury waved his bat and, with deceptive ease, played out a near maiden over from Smith, dropping the last ball at his feet and taking a very short single to keep the bowling again, while Gauvinier groaned in exasperation. There was still half an hour to go before tea. If they couldn't get the last wicket soon there'd be a pile of runs on the board for Tillingfold to get, judging by the way Dewbury was seeing the ball now. He decided to play safe.

'Thank you, Frank.' He held up his hand to Hunter, who was preparing to bowl the new over. 'I think Fred had better have a go.'

Hunter, furious at being taken off, jerked the ball to him awkwardly, remembering his two wickets in the first over and conveniently forgetting the seventeen hit off him in the next. 'Got to give his bloody pals a go, no matter what,' he said to himself, just loud enough for Gauvinier to hear if he wanted to, which he didn't.

Fred Bason's mild off-spin (leg-breaks of course to the left-hander) were not likely to disturb Dewbury in his present mood, but at least, Gauvinier reckoned, he would be more accurate than the mercurial Hunter. Oddly enough though, Bason liked bowling to left-handers, as he could move the ball away from the bat and there was always a chance of a catch in the slips.

Dewbury played his first two balls carefully back along the pitch. Then, stepping out, he hit him back safely over his head for two runs. Bason's fourth ball turned towards the off, and Dewbury, sweeping across the spin skied it towards mid-wicket. Either Trine, running across from deep mid-on, or White, closing rapidly from the square leg boundary, could have caught it easily. Gauvinier yelled 'Trine!' as the young man was closer to the ball, but White, calling 'mine' at the same moment, did not hear him and failed to stop. As the ball came down they converged, caught sight of each other simultaneously, and checked, letting the ball fall between them. The batsmen crossed for an easy two.

'After you, Claude.'

'No, after you Cecil.'

The time-honoured joke wafted mockingly from the pavilion, and all Tillingfold felt foolish for the unfortunate fielders. But it was another two runs on the board, and Gauvinier felt the frustration every captain feels when the last pair begin to make a stand.

Dewbury took a single off the fifth ball, bringing up the one hundred and thirty, and leaving Boggs to cope with the last which he did by his number three method. He left the bat in the blockhole and allowed the ball to hit it. No runs.

Bobby totted up Dewbury's score. 'He's got thirty-two already,' he said dolefully. 'He might get his fifty at this rate.'

Dewbury took two fours off Smith's next over, one a square cut standing up and the other a rather lucky inside edge to the fine leg boundary. Smith also conceded a no-ball. But this time Dewbury was unable to protect Boggs from facing a full over from Bason. The little man conferred with the tall Jamaican, standing incongruously together in the middle of the pitch.

'Ten minutes to go before tea,' he said. 'I'll try to give you the bowling so's you can get your fifty.'

'Just you stay there, man.'

But in his eagerness to help, Boggs actually moved up the pitch to Bason's next ball and swung his bat at it. He missed, but the move was so unexpected that Deacon fumbled the easy stumping chance, the ball slipping through his gloves and rolling away on the leg side. Gauvinier's groan of dismay turned into a shout as Dewbury, yelling 'Come on, Andy,' hurtled down the pitch.

Deacon, flinging his right glove aside, scuttled after the ball, and, grabbing it, turned and flung it hard to Bason at the bowler's wicket. Bason, taking it as casually as if he were catching a lobbed tennis ball, removed the bails, with the scampering Boggs a good yard away from safety.

'Howzat!' split the blue sky; up went the umpire's finger, and Raveley were all out for a hundred and thirty-eight. Dewbury, with forty not out, the best score of the innings, led the players in to tea, grinning hugely at the applause which echoed round the field.

'Pity he didn't get his fifty,' said Groat, once more leaning out to call, 'One thirty-eight, ten, two.' And the bowlers crowded into the little scorebox, straining to see their averages as the scorers tried to calculate them.

'That blasted last wicket put on thirty-five runs,' Gauvinier grumbled to Verrall.

'Ar. Hundred and thirty-eight. That'll take some getting,' responded the carpenter. 'What are their bowlers like?'

'Pretty useful, I think, but not as good as young Smith. Well played, Joe – there's more than one way of killing the cat, eh?'

'You don't often get a second chance like that,' answered Deacon. 'He must have thought he was out, he was so slow off the mark. But did you see old Fred, then? Calm as you please, just like he was at the seaside.'

'Yes, he made it look easy. Come on, we'll be missing our tea.'

Chapter 7

At every AGM of the Cricket Club, Colonel Sir Edgar Trine made a point of thanking the ladies of Tillingfold for their devoted and regular assistance in providing teas. They were no empty words, for Tillingfold teas were renowned the length and breadth of the county. Once upon a time, Jennings the local bakery had regularly supplied them as part of its catering business; but as the bakery grew, the catering side diminished, and indeed the Cricket Club's contract was such a small one that it was hardly worthwhile. It was also too expensive to import caterers from outside.

In similar circumstances, many clubs made do with cardboard boxes of ham sandwiches wrapped in plastic, with orange juice and with water slopped into glasses, but, as Gauvinier had said, a man needed a good cup of tea after he'd been running about the field all afternoon. So he'd approached his own wife, Rosie Hunter and one or two more, and asked them if they could do something to help. Rosie had taken on the basic organization, and between them the wives had arranged a rota. It became something of a competition between them, to see who could provide the best tea at the price. The club charged each player on both sides twenty-five pence, and each week handed over the £5.50 to the ladies. They bought the ingredients, made the tea, cut the sandwiches and baked the cakes. And then they came along on Saturday afternoons to fill the teacups, enduring the men's banter with the utmost good humour. They even took on the chore that Gauvinier found so distasteful, collecting the twenty-five pence from each player before he left the table. (The umpires and the scorers got their tea free.) And they usually had enough left over to sell some to those spectators who felt like a bite and some refreshment.

Colin Verral had helped to solve part of the problem of costs. He'd saved the end pieces of wood from a whole winter of his carpentry business, and had spent a weekend measuring, cutting and sandpapering. He then went along to the AGM and, when they reached 'any other business', he got to his feet.

'Mr Chairman,' he said, shyly. 'It's twenty years since I joined this club and every one of those twenty years there's been a moan about the price of cups and saucers and plates. So I'd like to make a presentation to the Club that'll help. If you wouldn't mind waiting a moment.'

He went out to his little mini-van, and returned carrying a large cardboard box. It looked heavy. He plonked it on the floor in front of the chairman's table and held up two small squares of wood, each about nine inches across.

'There's thirty platters here,' he said, 'all cut and sanded. They'll never break and you can wash 'em down and leave 'em to dry. Now all you need is decent size mugs to give a man's drink o' tea and do away with saucers.'

When he'd got over his first surprise, Sir Edgar had accepted the gift graciously on behalf of the Club, frowning severely at one or two gigglers. So now, for several seasons, the long white-clothed tables in the pavilion had been laid for tea with the wood platters, together with blue and yellow Denby mugs. It was a pleasant sight, and a great talking point and, as they'd found, strictly practical. Visiting teams always looked forward to tea-time at Tillingfold, and, it must be said, so did most of the home side too.

'Whew, what a spread, Peter,' said Troughton, as he sat down next to Gauvinier. 'I know what you're trying to do – slow us down so we won't be able to chase the ball this evening.'

The table was indeed attractive – egg and watercress sandwiches, ham sandwiches, bread and butter, two sorts of jam, and plates of cakes – spread at intervals along the table. The players, clumping on the wood floor in their boots, queued up to take their mugs of tea (they helped themselves to milk and sugar) from the big urns which stood at each end. Then they shuffled into their places, in no particular order, Tillingfold and Raveley jumbled up together – and at first there was comparative silence as thirsts were quenched, or hungers eased, according to individual need.

'Bloody good idea, these platters.'

'Bit odd, eatin' off wood.'

'I dunno, they used to in the old days.'

'Nice drop of tea, this.'

'Ah yes, a man needs a good drop of tea after being out there in the heat.'

'You always get a good tea at Tillingfold.'

'Who baked these scones?'

'Dunno. Rosie Hunter, I think. Hey, Frank. Your wife make these scones?'

A nod. Hunter's mouth was full of salmon sandwich, which he liked.

'I must get her to tell my old girl how to make 'em. They don't cook now like they used to.'

'I dunno, there's not much wrong with this lot, is there?'

Rosie Hunter, presiding over her tea-urn, said to Fred Bason, who was first as usual for a refill, 'It never fails to amaze me where you men put it all. Every Saturday I swear we've made enough for an army, but it all disappears like magic. Every time.'

'You shouldn't do such a good job,' he replied, quietly.

'Everything all right with you, girl?' A glance down the table.

'Oh yes, I suppose so, Fred.' She sighed.

'Well, let me know if there's anything I can do. Anything.' He took his mug of tea and, touching her arm, moved back to his place.

'How's that new estate of yours, Phil?' This was Bason the builder again, calling across and down the table to Troughton, the solicitor. The players in between them courteously muted their conversation to listen.

'Coming on fine, thanks Fred,' Troughton called back. He was handling the conveyancing of a high-class development on the outskirts of Raveley.

'You could divert that stream at the back and put in some nice ponds – it'd make a change.'

'Oh, I don't know.' Troughton considered the idea. 'I don't think the architect's thought of that.'

'Not even to hatch a few more duck's eggs?'

There was a burst of laughter at the ancient joke, old as cricket itself.

'Damn you, Fred, I'll get my own back for that,' Troughton said, as he wiped the laughter from his eyes.

'Now now, young Norm, don't laugh so much, you'll do yourself an injury. Just because you fooled the old fox here.'

'Ah now,' said young Smith. 'Mr Gauvinier told me what to bowl, so I did.'

Gauvinier, not wanting to give the young man a swollen head, told him. 'You won't have it so easy in future, you know. But it was a damn good over.'

'Yes it was,' said Troughton, with feeling. 'But we were unlucky to lose Dick Spencer, just when he was getting set.'

'What d' you mean, lucky? I bowled for that. But, my goodness, that was some catch.'

Spencer, sitting a few places away, caught the conversation.

'That must have been the best catch I've seen this year. I hit it with everything, and there he was, popping up out of nowhere holding up the ball. You must have dived twenty feet,' he said to Paul, who was in the middle of a large piece of Swiss roll. 'Did it hurt your hand much?'

Paul, unable to speak, shook his head, blushing.

'Oh, he's all right on nice dry hot days like this one. But you should see him when it's a bit wet, like. He's more like a drowned duck, then.'

Verrall was referring to a never-to-be-forgotten incident in a match against one of the villages in the Kent hills. The sloping pitch with its chalk base dried out amazingly fast and play was possible there even after the most violent storms. On such a day White had chased after a ball which streaked towards the boundary, throwing up a little spume of spray from the wet grass as it went. Going flat out, he'd caught up with it, and had put his foot out to try and stop it. But instead he'd trodden on the ball and his speed had carried him headlong over the boundary on to rough ground. To the whole side's astonishment, he'd disappeared completely headfirst. A minute or so later, he'd emerged from a deep ditch, covered with brambles, scratched, bleeding and completely soaked, like Neptune rising from the deep. Verrall, who'd been chasing after him, forgot the ball that had been stopped short of the boundary and collapsed with laughter. The batsmen ran five.

Jess found himself between Mohinder and Dewbury. He leant back in his chair and offered them a cigarette.

'Don't smoke, thanks,' said Mohinder, but Dewbury took one of the long slim sobranies with a grin. 'Thanks, man, I can't usually afford these.' He took an experimental drag, and coughed. 'Not sure as I'd want to.'

'That was a good knock of yours. How d' you like our cricket?'

'Never known any better, man.'

'What, not even in . . . where d' you come from?'

'Jamaica, but that was ten years ago.'

'How you making out over here?'

'Cricket or altogether?'

'Altogether.'

'Not so bad. My wife works at the hospital as a sister. I drive the hospital lorry.'

'Would you ever want to go back? What did you do before you came over?'

'Man, I dream of going back every night. I was a farmer. Last year I saved up to go and see my family. They all wanted me to stay. But what am I to do? My two daughters are at school here. If I go back, the school is not so good for them. They do well here. My wife do well. So I stay.'

'What don't you like about England?'

'The weather, man. And the town.'

'But you like cricket though?'

'When I make forty I like cricket. And I meet people, have good tea, good talk, make a few runs. It's the life, man.'

'Well, I think so, too,' said Jess, slightly embarrassed by such intensity. 'Let me get you another mug of tea.'

'Can I have a word with you, Mr Mitterman?'

'Surely, Bill. What can I do for you?'

'Can we go outside? It's a bit private.'

They took their tea and strolled out into the sunlight, which made them flinch after the comparative gloom of the pavilion. They made an odd pair; Budgeon with his one-legged shuffle, his old cream flannels and his broad brown face; Mitterman immaculate in white, with striped blazer and cream silk scarf at his neck.

'It's two things, really.' Budgeon was hot with embarrassment at having to make his confession. Their roles of a few minutes ago were completely reversed. Budgeon the expert cricketer, natural ballplayer; Mitterman the accountant, at home in a sea of figures, clumsy and incompetent on a cricket field. Yet it was the cricket field that gave Budgeon the confidence to approach Mitterman.

'I've made a hell of a mess with my income tax and my VAT. And now I'm getting mixed up with the Patents Office too. I just don't seem to be able to cope with all the bloody paper.'

'Of course I'll help, Bill. But I'm a pro, you know. I cost money.'

'That's what's bothering me, Mr Mitterman. I know I can't afford to pay the fees. How much are they?'

'Well, from what you tell me I am assuming you can't afford *not* to pay me, Bill. But seriously, you needn't worry about that just now. Let me come along and sort you out. I've a pretty good idea that you'll able to pay me easily enough from what I save you. Come and have another cup of tea. No, don't thank me until we've got you fixed up. What's all this about a patent? What have you been up to?'

Back in the pavilion, the piles on the plates were diminishing; several of the men had refilled their mugs with tea and were sitting back smoking and swapping cricket stories. Gauvinier, who'd stopped smoking a couple of years before, refused a cigarette from Troughton.

'No thanks, I don't any more.'

'Wish I could stop. I envy you your will-power.'

'It wasn't that, it was my wife's. She went at me so much that it was either stop smoking or leave home. And I wasn't quite ready for that.'

'Does it worry you? Me smoking, I mean.'

'Not a bit. But I confess that it's a bit harder at a time like this. You know, when you're sitting back relaxed.'

'I know just what you mean.' He blew out a cloud of smoke.

'How's that hand of yours?'

'Fine. No bother. I was bloody lucky, you know.'

He held up his left hand for inspection, pointing out the faint line of a scar, where the palm joins the wrist.

'That's good,' said Troughton. 'I've been dining out on that story ever since, telling people what a dangerous game cricket is.'

They both laughed. They'd been playing in the same team at a tiny village, Beaubusson, whose ground was situated on an old country estate. Cricket had been played there a hundred years or more, on a field fenced off by barbed wire from the sheep and cows that grazed the surrounding pastures.

Gauvinier had completed his innings ('Caught behind for two, I recall') and was lazing in the sun when he noticed, on the far side of the ground, a sheep which appeared to be in trouble. He liked to stroll round the picturesque ground, anyway, so he'd wandered round, to discover that the sheep had become entangled in a loose strand of barbed wire, and was trapped.

The wire had caught in the wool on the sheep's belly, and had twisted and tangled until it appeared held by a two-inch thick rope of wool and wire together. Gauvinier had called up reinforcements, and he and Troughton, armed with a blunt penknife, had tried to free the terrified animal.

They found the only way they could handle the sheep, which was kicking vigorously, was to turn it on its back and hold its head down with a knee. Then Gauvinier pulled the wool and the wire away from its body, while Troughton tried to cut the tangle away with the knife. The knife had slipped and slashed across Gauvinier's wrist. Instantly blood spurted, covering them both, and abandoning the sheep they'd run for the pavilion, Gauvinier holding his wrist with his right hand, blood dripping down his short and his flannels. He wasn't much hurt, but Troughton had driven him to the nearest hospital, where he'd had six stitches put in by a Turkish doctor, who had laughed and told him to join the Anti-Blood Sports League.

'I wonder what happened to that bloody sheep,' said Troughton.

'Probably still there, starved to death,' said Gauvinier. 'I must go and sort out some sort of order. See you later.'

Spencer was swapping cricket stories with Trine. '. . . and there was the cricket correspondent who interviewed one of England's best-known women cricketers after the first Women's Test. He was intrigued to see in the dressing-room all the usual paraphernalia – pads, bats, gloves, boxes and so on. "Tell me," he asked the lady, "Why do you wear a box – the same type of protector as men do?" "It hurts us just as much as it does you men when we get hit there," the lady replied. "But we don't call them boxes in women's cricket. We call them manhole covers." '

'Talking of cricket writers, you know what they used to say of Swanton, that he was the only cricket correspondent in the world who would go along to a match in his Rolls-Royce praying for rain. Then he could turn on the windscreen wipers and let the crowd watch him, instead of the players.'

Trine laughed. 'Oh, yes, old Jim lorded it over the rest, all right. But he knew his cricket. And loved it too. He must be brassed off at what's happened to the England team in the last couple of seasons. Where the hell the cricketers have gone, the Lord only knows.'

Bason came into the conversation. 'It's the Labour Government. Oh, I don't mean this one particularly, but ever since the war the education in this country's been going down hill. All this blasted comprehensive business. The schools don't have time for cricket any more. There's no coaching, the teachers don't give a damn for anything except their spare time. It's no wonder there are no youngsters in English cricket any more.'

'Oh, I don't know.' Spencer helped the county ground staff during the Christmas and Easter courses at the county ground. 'I agree to some extent that the schools have lost interest, but that's been taken up by the clubs in a very big way.

'Down at Hove last Christmas there were plenty of kids. And at Easter we had over four hundred boys from eight to sixteen or so at the nets. Didn't know what to do with them.'

'The gap *has* been taken up by the clubs,' someone else chipped in. The conversation became general. 'Look at Raveley, now. We've more youngsters in the club than ever before; and we've sometimes turned out three youth teams of a week-end.'

'I'm not sure you should blame education as such,' said Radnam. 'If cricket's wrong at the top it means it's wrong at county level. I blame the system of allowing overseas players into the county teams.'

It was a favourite hobby horse. There was a chorus of assent.

'It don't give an English lad a chance of getting in,' said Hunter. 'They'll never find good number three, four and five batsmen for England while your Richardses, your Kanhais, your Procters and your Davisons are playing.'

'I don't know,' Bason said. 'Cricket would have been in a helluva mess without them. They've certainly lifted the standard of the game and brought in the crowds.'

'Oh, one-day cricket's done that more than the overseas players,' said another voice. 'But it's one-day cricket that's ruined our batsmen, and bowlers . . .'

'Never . . .' 'Course it had . . .' The argument raged on.

Young Trine slipped out to take tea to his parents in their deck chairs, much enjoying his mother's suppressed distaste at being handed a mug. He glanced casually along the boundary line, noting with satisfaction from a flash of nylon that the girls were still there. Perhaps they'd like a mug of tea too. He grinned to himself. Or maybe a drink at 'The Dog and Duck' after the match. He'd have to go for a stroll round the boundary a bit later. It was part of his basic honesty that he didn't really expect to be at the wicket for any length of time.

He was relieved from his filial duty by the arrival of Harry Broome, slightly glazed around the eyes, with his American tourists in tow.

'Sir Edgar, excuse me, but may I introduce two American visitors . . . Mr Granville T. Johnson and Mrs Johnson, from Texas . . . Sir Edgar and Lady Trine. I've been trying to explain cricket to them, Sir Edgar, and I thought you'd do it so much better than I can. Mr Johnson owns a ranch near Houston.'

'Pleased to meet you, indeed, sir. Pleased to meet you. Rancher, eh?'

'Yes indeed, sir. Thirty thousand acres of beef cattle – and a couple of oil wells. Same name as the former president, sir, and same party. But no relation. No, sir.'

He gazed round at the field, the green grass, the white sight-screens and the white flannels as the players moved out from their tea.

'This is England as I've heard about it, sir. But I can't quite get the hang of the game yet ...'

Sir Edgar wished he could remember off pat the classic instruction for Americans. It goes something like this:

The fielders go out. The batsmen go in. When a batsman is out, he comes in and another batsman goes out to go in. He is out if he's caught or bowled out or run out. When this has happened ten times the side's all out and the fielders come in. Then the other side goes in and when they're all out they all come in and the game's all over.

Instead he contented himself with 'Why don't you and your wife have some tea and come and join us? We can explain it as it goes along.'

Young Trine sauntered away down the boundary, his eye on the two girls, sitting on their rug and helping themselves to tea from a hamper. He had his opening gambit prepared.

'Sorry I nearly trod on you,' he said as he approached, dropping easily on one knee. 'I was distracted by the sight of two girls watching a cricket match by themselves. Are you with anybody?'

'Oh, you're the one who dropped the catch,' said the blonde, looking straight through him. 'No, we came to see Ahmed.'

'Ahmed? ... Oh Mohinder, the Raveley man, you mean? He's a good cricketer, I'm told.'

'Hullo, Trine, I see you've met my friends.' Mohinder's urbanity was all-embracing. Trine, put out by the snub and what he regarded as familiarity, tried to make an excuse to leave, but was forestalled.

'Have you introduced yourselves? No? This is Mr Trine, my

dears. Trine, the blonde is Alison; the brunette is Sally. Alison came to see me make a century and was disappointed. Sally wants to meet Albert Jess.'

'Call me Edward,' said Trine in some confusion. 'Or Teddy. Everyone does. D' you want to meet Jess? He'll be opening the batting, I expect, but when he's out I'll bring him along.'

'Where do you bat, Trine?'

'Oh, well down. Seven or eight, I should think. That's quite high enough for my methods.'

But at that moment a hail came from the pavilion. 'Trine, get your pads on, please.'

'Oh lor',' Trine got to his feet, flushing with pleasure. 'It seems I'm elevated. See you later.' And he trotted off to be told by the captain that he'd be going in number three, after first wicket went down, to see if he could keep the score moving along.

'We can't afford to get behind the clock,' Gauvinier said. 'We've got to average over a run a minute.'

He continued writing in the scorebook. Tillingfold's batting order, he always maintained to himself, should be dictated solely by the merits of the players and the needs of the game; but privately, to himself and in conversation with Oliver Fanshawe, he admitted that there was often more than an element of political necessity about the selection.

'It's just like a Labour Prime Minister picking his Cabinet,' he told Fanshawe. 'If Bason's taken a wicket or two, then Hunter goes in before Bason. That's Frank 'n' Fred. If Hunter's had a good bowl, then it'll be Fred 'n' Frank.'

'Deacon's a better bat than Colin Verrall; but Colin's so willing and does so much for the club that I feel mean keeping him down at number nine – and of course you know where I'd like to play James.'

'Permanent number twelve, I suppose,' Fanshawe grunted. 'Never mind, Peter. He's got to come good one day – he's desperately keen behind it all.'

Today's selection was complicated for Gauvinier by the number of runs Tillingfold had to score to win – a hundred and thirty-nine. As they'd managed to dismiss Raveley in time for an early tea, they'd have two hours and ten minutes in which to score the runs. Ample time in this class of cricket, but Gauvinier was too sceptical of the strength of his batting to do more than hope for the best.

Eventually, with much thought, he completed the list and punctiliously, as always, copied it out on a separate sheet of paper, to pin up on the changing room door.

1 Mitterman
2 Jess
3 Trine
4 Bason
5 Hunter
6 White
7 Gauvinier
8 Deacon
9 Verrall
10 Smith
11 Budgeon

'Tail-end charlie, please, Bill. But don't be surprised if I make a switch.' It was his habit to change the batting order without warning during the innings if he felt it would be worthwhile. Strangely, once the batting order had been actually published, the players' feelings seemed rarely to be hurt by any sudden tactical switch.

'Pads on, James. Mr Jess, would you mind opening with Mitterman here? I know you're a bit rusty, but I'd like to throw you in at the deep end. We've got to show them a bit of class early on.'

'Okay, skipper, I don't mind. But you're taking a bit of a chance, you know. And for Pete's sake call me Albert.'

'Righto, Albert.' Gauvinier laughed. 'And if you knew what I do about the rest of our batting, you wouldn't think it was so much of a chance.'

'Hold on a bit there, skipper.' Bason's hearty chuckle broke in behind him. 'We're not so bad as all that. With Mr Trine here good for a quick fifty and me to hold the fort, it's a cinch.'

'Especially with Bill here at number eleven. Don't know anyone better to prop up the order.'

'Ah, Bill won't be needed today. I feel like a few myself . . .'

And so, with feeble wisecracks and hearty laughter, they built up each other's spirits. For, as the innings started, each of them felt as nervous as a boy.

Gauvinier had served part of his war as a parachutist, and he always likened this part of the match to the waiting before a jump. He recalled the training instructor's voice, rapping out the words and repetitive oaths in the grating, impinging fashion adopted by NCOs the world over.

'Nah. Yer goin' to feel nervous. Let any man tell yer he's not nervous at some time before a jump and I'll tell yer he's a liar. If yer say yer not shit-scared, then I'll tell yer yer a liar. It might not be at the same time. Some'll feel it when they draws their 'chute. Some'll get it when they're kittin' up; or when they're gettin' on the plane. Or when they stand up 'n' hitch on the static line. Or when they hear "Red on – stand in the door . . . green on – *go*!' If yer unlucky then yer'll be wettin' yer britches all the time. It doesn't matter whether it's yer first jump or yer nine hundred and fiftieth – yer always nervous at some time.'

In much the same way every batsman feels a tightening of the stomach, a quickening of the breath and a surge of hope at some time before going in to bat. Some find it in putting on their pads; others when they go out to lounge in the deck chairs and to 'get their eyes used to the light'; others still when the preceding batsman's wicket falls, and you stand up to put on your batting gloves, trying to look casual and unconcerned. Or it might be during the second longest walk in the world, out to the wicket. (The longest is the walk back with a duck to your name.) Or it might be when you take your guard, or when the bowler runs towards you.

Troughton put his head round the dressing room door. 'Just checking, Peter. It is stumps at seven-thirty, isn't it? Not the twenty overs lark?'

'That's right, Phil. Seven-thirty by Oliver's watch.'

'Or earlier, if we can make it!'

The fielding side has its moments of anxiety, too.

Chapter 8

Tillingfold, like many thousands of village clubs, had always taken very slowly to innovations designed to speed up the game, or to amending the laws to redress some imbalance between bowler and batsman. Fanshawe argued, and Gauvinier backed him strongly, that there was little wrong with cricket at the grass roots and it didn't need tinkering with to make it more 'acceptable' to the public.

'If the game's sick, it's sick at county and national level,' Fanshawe would say. 'If people won't go to watch it any more, it's because they've killed the game at the top. They've coached the strokes out of the players and rolled the pace out of the pitches, and then they moan that we don't have any attacking batsmen and we don't have any fast bowlers. So they make up little gimmicks like the twenty overs rule to give the big boys a chance a finish a game.

'Three days is long enough for any game – and if it's a draw at the end of that time, it's a draw. All these bonus points, and fining people for slow over-rates – they're ridiculous. Why, when they wanted to hustle, Leicestershire bowled twenty-four overs in the last hour and won the match ... and more than once the side that's been a hundred or more behind on the first innings has landed up with more points than the blokes who led them. It doesn't make sense. It's turning cricket into a statistician's paradise.'

They hadn't much more time for the new one-day competitions, although it was acknowledged that the Gillette Cup, the John Player League and the Benson and Hedges Competition had done a great deal to stimulate interest in cricket.

'We don't need the sort of gimmick that means someone's got to win, no matter what. We get results most times at Tillingfold and it's rare to see a village side tamely trying for a draw. They're usually not good enough in the first place, and in the second, if they try it too often they won't get asked again. We'll drop them from the fixture list. You try batting through after tea-time, no matter how few runs you've got, and see what happens. If a side manages to hang on for a draw, that's sometimes as near a win as winning; and a tie's the most exciting finish you can ever get to a cricket match.

'We often get more than three hundred runs scored in an afternoon – once we had more than five hundred runs scored in five hours' play. What more could you ask?'

What more, indeed, thought Gauvinier, as he watched his opening batsmen walk purposefully together to the wicket, while Troughton deployed his men in attacking positions round the field.

Mitterman, tall, portly and dignified, made an imposing figure as he took guard immaculately. 'Leg stump, please, Mr Umpire, a shade towards the centre.' The Tillingfold cap, a legacy of the past, looked ridiculous on most modern-day cricketers, particularly the youngsters like Smith and White with their long, thick curls. 'Like a pimple on a haystack' was the usual more polite description. But on Mitterman's short-back-and-sides, the sky-blue cap achieved the archaic dignity of the Boz cartoons on the stairways at Lord's. His cream shirt and his flannels, folded carefully and tucked into white woollen socks over white suède boots, both came from Harrods. He wore foam-backed pads of the latest design, and his batting gloves were of the revolutionary paddle-backed variety favoured (and promoted) by England's cricket captain. Mitterman also affected one of the new 'scooped out' bats with its long flash of red paint down the back. It had cost him not far short of £30, and it was covered in silicone, which rendered unnecessary the old-fashioned treatment with linseed oil.

Jess, standing at the bowler's end, thought irreverently that Mitterman looked like one of those colour supplement pictures of A *Complete Cricketer*, portrayed in stylized fashion with little lines leading to boxes containing the price of each article of clothing so marked – shirt, £14; trousers, £21; 'box', £3.50;

and so on. Jess himself had dug out the old flannels he used at school, wore a medallion on a silver chain round his neck, and had borrowed the rest of his gear from the club bag. As he was not very tall the pads looked slightly too big on him. The batting gloves were stained and hardened by the sweat of many hands. They had once been kid, with green rubber spikes like miniature tank traps sewn along each finger for protection. His boots were old and cracked, and he'd found a short-handled bat in the bag, a much-used favourite which had been through many battles for Tillingfold and was looking a little the worse for wear.

Mitterman looked as if he were dressed as a cricketer. Jess looked as if he was one. Mitterman surveyed the scene with unruffled dignity, while his stomach churned and his mind was choked with fright – of the bowler, of the ball, of making himself ridiculous. Jess fidgeted and fretted, playing imaginary strokes with his bat, straightening his pads, tightening his straps, and he generally resembled a cat on hot bricks. But in fact he'd forgotten his nerves the moment they'd left the pavilion. All his actions were subconscious – he just wanted to get at the bowling.

Mitterman settled himself at the crease, then stood back and surveyed the field placing. Raveley's captain, Troughton, was fortunate in having two fairly quick bowlers with whom to open, the schoolboys Agnew and Graves. Of the two, Agnew had the more bite but was less accurate. He also took an inordinately long run, measuring out twenty-five paces, setting down his mark and then retreating a further fifteen yards or so before turning to begin his run-up. It infuriated Gauvinier, for an over from Agnew could take as much as five minutes to bowl, and that meant Raveley could shut up one end and drag out time if they wanted to play for a draw.

It did not look, however, as if Troughton or the Raveley side in general were too much impressed by the young man's speed. Dewbury, the wicketkeeper, stationed himself no farther back than had Deacon for Smith's fast-medium; and Troughton set an orthodox field. There were two slips, a gully, third man and fine leg, cover point, mid-off, mid-on, a mid-wicket half way to the boundary and a silly mid-on close up. Mitterman settled back to his stance, correct and elegant, left arm forward and both eyes square to the pitch.

'Play,' called the Raveley umpire, and from forty yards behind him Agnew began his long run-up. He accelerated with short, quick steps, settled down to two long ones, then broke stride again with a curious little shuffle before lengthening his pace to the wicket and bowling with a high, youthful action. Mitterman watched the ball fizz towards him and moved his left foot forward (but not far enough across the pitch) to play defensively. The ball, which was well outside the off stump, struck the face of the bat and looped back gently in the air, just to the leg side of the pitch. Had Agnew followed through straight, it would have been a 'dolly', but his run had carried him well to the off. He checked, twisted in the air and tried to leap up backwards to his right. The ball just missed his fingers and he fell in a cloud of dust in the centre of the pitch. The ball bounded past the umpire and rolled slowly on, while Mitterman, after a 'wait' – 'no' – 'yes' sequence ran a comfortable single.

Agnew picked himself up, felt himself all over for injury and apparently finding none trudged back towards his mark looking a little shaken. Jess, receiving his first ball, was happy to let it go by harmlessly outside the leg stump; and he was even more happy to turn the next one, which was short and on his body, round to fine leg for a single.

Leaning back in his deck chair in front of the pavilion, Gauvinier let the air escape from his lungs. He felt he'd been holding his breath since the first ball. He leaned towards Bason, who'd taken the next chair and was sitting with his pads on, his bat and gloves on the ground beside him. Gauvinier always insisted that his team should be padded up two wickets before they were needed – in other words, batsman number five should get himself prepared when the first wicket fell, even though he was not due to bat until the third wicket had fallen. Gauvinier loathed the inefficiency and, as he considered it, rudeness of making the opposing team wait for the next batsman, as often happened when a side lost two or three wickets quickly. And Raveley, with a solicitor as captain, were notorious for sticking to the letter of the law and had once appealed successfully against a new batsman for taking more than two minutes to appear after the last man was out.

'Why on earth does that young man take such a hell of a long run?' he asked Bason rhetorically. 'Look at him – the first twenty yards are all wasted. He'd bowl just as fast and twice as accurately off half the run. Phil Troughton should tell him.'

The young man under inspection, unaware of derogatory comments, delivered a full-pitched ball on the off stump, which Mitterman, aiming to drive to mid-on, actually sliced off the outside edge of the bat wide of gully. The batsmen crossed for an easy two as Brewster sprinted from cover to save the boundary.

'The old boy looks in form,' Bason commented. 'He's actually hit two out of three.'

'Don't speak too soon.' Gauvinier hadn't a great deal of faith in Mitterman's prowess. 'Anyway, he's not so old. He's younger then you are.'

'He just acts it. But he's no opening bat, and you know it.'

Gauvinier tried to defend himself against the implied criticism, but without much conviction. The trouble was that you just couldn't find the people with the time and energy, not to say the inclination, to help out with the difficult jobs these days. There was no fun in being secretary, with the endless correspondence and frustrations. It was almost worse if, like James, you were coping with other people's inefficiency and casualness, particularly in the matter of money. But that should be no reason for playing the chap when he wasn't good enough, and Gauvinier knew it.

'Oh, come on, Fred, James isn't as bad ... Oh no!' He was stopped in mid-sentence.

The fifth ball of Agnew's over had gone through fast, nipping off the pitch, and, beating Mitterman's nasty stroke, had hit him on the right thigh muscle above the pad. Mitterman, dropping his bat and rubbing his upper leg in considerable pain, hadn't heard the appeal nor seen the umpire's finger go up for lbw.

'Howzat, Dad ... Out, son,' said Hunter savagely, for the Raveley umpire had something of a reputation for biased decisions. He was young Agnew's uncle.

'Steady, Frank.' Gauvinier spoke hastily. 'He looked well in front.'

'Yes, but it was far too high, you could see it from here.'

And indeed Mitterman, who came off the field limping, was rubbing the damaged leg well above the pad. There was a little sympathetic applause, and Gauvinier called 'Hard luck, James. We thought that looked a bit high.'

The next man in, Edward Trine, had jumped to his feet the moment the umpire's finger went up, and was striding to the wicket well before Bobby Bewers could call out 'Four, one, three.' He waved his bat airily towards the girls, who were, he noticed, still displaying a satisfying amount of leg. 'I'll see if I can land one in Alison's lap,' he thought, 'particularly if that smooth blighter's bowling.'

Like many unsound cricketers (and many sound ones for that matter) Trine relied a great deal on fortune; and he offered up little sacrifices to his gods, especially at the start of his innings. He would make his block in the shape of a 'T', for instance; and in between balls would circle the wicket in a clockwise direction, holding his bat in front of his face like a pikestaff. Trine was not alone. The great England wicket-keeper, Alan Knott, is renowned for his mannerism of touching the bails with his left hand before facing up to the ball, as if to reassure himself they are still there. Greig, the England captain, touches first the peak of his cap and then the top of his pads before taking his stance; and another well-known but not-to-be-named county cricketer has a habit of adjusting his protective box with a heave, bending both knees at the same time.

So he hammered out his blockhole with the toe of his bat, made his little clockwise tour of the wicket, and drove confidently and airily at his first ball. And missed it.

'Another coat of paint,' observed Dewbury to his slips, 'and the young man would have been on a hat-trick.'

Trine, pleased at not having given a catch to the slips and at not having been bowled, decided his luck was in today and smiled amiably around him.

The ginger-haired Harry Graves, Raveley's second opening bowler, was the fielder who had been substituted for Norman at the start of Raveley's innings. He had the makings of a good county bowler. He could swerve the ball and cut it off the pitch in the same way as Budgeon; but although steady, he would never match Budgeon's instinctive feel for the game and his insight into a batsman's temperament. Despite this, he would bowl his heart out all afternoon, and would never be particularly easy to 'get away'.

His bowling today, however, was something of a disaster. Harry Graves had a weakness for cucumber sandwiches which amounted to a passion, and with the help and encouragement of both his own side and his opponents had demolished almost a plateful of Mrs Rosie Hunter's cucumber sandwiches during the tea interval. He'd washed them down with a couple of mugs of hot tea, three teaspoonfuls of sugar in each. In consequence the sudden and violent activity of bowling had stirred his stomach, which was not fond of cucumber sandwiches at the best of times, into active revolt.

His first ball to Albert Jess landed on a length just wide of the leg stump. Jess, playing forward carefully, missed it, and it cannoned off his pads out past the square leg umpire for two leg byes. Graves, breathing puffily through his mouth, caught the ball on the return and doubled up suddenly with a griping pain shooting across his stomach.

'I'll be all right,' he panted, red-faced, as his concerned teammates clustered around. He rubbed hard at his stomach and shooed them back to their positions in the field.

His second ball was similar to the first, but this time Jess came down on it hard and true and drove it through the legside field for four runs, all along the ground. The on-drive looks the easiest shot in the book. But it is the shot for the connoisseur. Executed well, it is a stroke needing both footwork and timing, and one which gives a great deal of pleasure to the batsman. Even poor Graves, bent over double again with pain as he watched the ball speeding to the boundary, could appreciate its excellence.

More rubbing, and he ran to bowl his third ball. His gripe was seizing him like an iron band and he swung his arm over anyhow. The result was a slow, looping full toss which in normal circumstances Jess would have clouted to the boundary. But as he delivered the ball Graves collapsed in the bowler's crease and lay groaning, his arms clutched tight around him. Jess forgot all about the ball, dropped his bat and ran up the wicket as Fanshawe, the umpire, went down on his knees to help Graves.

Dewbury, the wicketkeeper, intent on the ball, caught it in his gloves and removed the bails, automatically appealing for the stumping at the same time; and up went Mr Tyler's finger: 'Out!'

To the spectators on the boundary it was as if a painting on glass had suddenly disintegrated. At one moment there was a cricket match. At the next, there was a huddle of white-clad figures round another lying on the floor. Fanshawe and Troughton made a cradle with their crossed hands, and, slowly, awkwardly, they carried the hunched-up body of Graves back into the pavilion. He was white-faced and obviously in great pain.

'Don't worry, Phil, we'll do what we can for him. The Colonel here'll run him over to the hospital. It looks like appendicitis to me. I'll get him fixed up and send you out a sub. Come on, young 'un. You'll be all right. You going to be sick?'

Graves managed a shake of the head: with his teeth clenched against the pain he couldn't speak. Colonel Trine, relieved at anything that would free him from the American tourists, was already on his way to get the car.

'Can we help? We're nurses.' Alison and Sally took charge competently. Gauvinier sent Norman Smith out to field as substitute for Raveley, and within three minutes the distraction was over, the unfortunate Graves on the way to the hospital, with Sally holding his head and Alison the whitewashbucket, so as not to soil the Colonel's Bentley.

Out on the field the tableau rearranged itself into a cricket match, but not before one or two small matters had been sorted out.

Jess went back to the crease and picked up his bat, ready to start all over again.

'Hey, Mister,' said Dewbury. 'You're out. I stumped you and the umpire he give you out.'

'Oh no,' said Jess, dismayed. 'You can't do that. I wasn't playing the ball. I went to help your mate.'

'What you say, Mr Umpire?' Dewbury looked to Mr Tyler standing at square leg. The umpire scratched his head.

'Don't really know,' he said. 'You appealed, I gave him out because he was out of his crease, so I suppose strictly he was out.'

Fanshawe's deep voice came from the bowler's wicket.

'The batsman is not out, Mr Umpire. That was a no-ball. I called it myself. The batsman cannot be given out off a no-ball.'

He turned towards the scorebox, walked a few paces and, cupping his hands around his mouth to make a megaphone, called, 'That last one was a no-ball.'

Groat waved back, and added one to the score. Leaning out he called 'ten up'. He grinned conspiratorially at Bobby. Eleven really, but nobody will know. What are they doing now?'

Fanshawe had called Troughton over to him. 'Mr Captain, the over was uncompleted. You must ask another bowler to deliver the four remaining balls.'

'All right, Mr Umpire. First time I've come across this one.' He called to Mohinder. 'Now's your chance, Ahmed. Four balls of the over to complete,' and he threw the ball over.

Mohinder, delighted at getting the ball so soon, told Fanshawe 'Right arm over the wicket', and called 'same field' to Troughton. He did not bother marking his run up – just strolled back a few paces, turned, ran in and whipped the ball down with amazing pace.

Jess, surprised by the speed of the ball and the suddenness of the delivery, stepped back and away from the lifting ball, jabbed at it, and touched it straight to the wicketkeeper. He was walking towards the pavilion almost before it disappeared into Dewbury's gloves. The big Jamaican flung it high in the air as he appealed.

'He might just as well ha' walked when he were stumped,' said Dewbury to Agnew, who was standing next to him in the slips. 'But he was lucky to get rid of that one. He could bat. You saw that drive off his legs?'

'Eleven for two, then,' said Agnew, watching the figures go up on the scoreboard. 'That's a good start. It looks like a piece of cake.'

'Oh man, never say that about cricket. The moment you think you got cricket taped, then it get up and hit you. Remember, we're a bowler down.'

Jess, disconsolate, slumped down on the bench in the changing room. 'Hanging my bat out to dry. Bloody tool.'

Fred Bason, the next man in, was possibly the best man in the side except Gauvinier for a crisis. With eleven runs on the board, the opening batsmen out and the third man yet to score, he didn't need Gauvinier's cautionary, 'Take it easy, Fred.'

He strolled casually to the wicket, his old bat looking as if it was made of dark oak rather than willow. His sleeves were rolled up to reveal massive forearms, his trousers held round his waist by an old brown tie. Colin Verrall, who during the week did most of Bason's carpentry under contract, sang out behind him, 'Come on, there, Mr five by five'; and Fred turned his big head, smiled his slow smile and said, 'Plenty of time, skinny.'

He took guard, inspected the field and waited for the first ball from Mohinder, who did his trick of walking back, wheeling suddenly and running in to bowl. Fred stepped back from his crease and held up a hand like a policeman on point duty.

'Sorry, bowler,' he called out as Mohinder, forced to halt in mid stride, turned and had to wait until Bason was ready again.

'First round to Fred,' Verrall said to Gauvinier. 'He won't catch Fred that way.'

Mohinder bowled, fast and straight, and Bason put his large foot down the pitch, planted his large bat next to it and played straight back; and then he did precisely the same to the next two balls. Fanshawe called 'Over'; and the Tillingfold team relaxed. The crisis, they felt, was over.

They were wrong. It seemed to Trine that he'd been in a long time; but in fact he'd faced only one ball. He blocked Agnew's first delivery, and drove the next firmly past mid-off. There was a comfortable two, but Trine, trying to force the pace, turned to go for a third. He overestimated the distance Brewster had to run – the ball was slowed up by the thicker grass in that part of the outfield – but even so he would have got home had not Brewster's throw hit the base of the wicket at the bowler's end. It was lucky, but it was the sort of thing that happened when a team was on its toes, going for every chance.

'Eleven for three,' Bobby called out mournfully. 'Sorry. Thirteen for three, last man two.'

Trine came in, black as thunder. He had nobody to blame but himself for getting out, and he felt miserable that he'd let the whole side down. He joined Jess and Mitterman in the changing room, unbuckling his pads and getting ready to change out of his flannels. They made such a composite picture of gloom that Gauvinier, coming in to pad up, couldn't help laughing.

'Cheer up, for goodness' sake. We're going to win this game,' he said.

'Bloody lucky if we get fifty at this rate,' said Trine.

'Not on your life. Fred 'n' Frank are going to score fifty each. You'll see. I feel it in my bones.'

'Never. One of them'll run the other out: or at least it won't be for want of trying.'

'Better than running yourself out, though, isn't it?'

Trine, who could never remain gloomy for long, laughed.

'Oh, I just wanted to nip over to the pub for a quick one. I lost my way. Run up!' He bellowed suddenly at the window pane.

Frank Hunter had hit his first ball, more or less intentionally, over the top of the slips' heads, and it was running towards the boundary. Boggs, chasing round from third man, stopped it with his foot before it rolled over the line, though his throw was so weak that Frank easily had time to make a fourth run. But Fred, leaning breathlessly on his bat, stopped him. 'Three's enough for me, Frank.' And Frank, not yet sufficiently immersed in the game to forget their rivalry, scowled and growled to himself, 'Wanted to pinch the bloody bowling, more like.'

Bason blocked the next two balls; then he leaned across, hardly moving his legs, and dabbed the fifth ball of the over hard down past point for a single, to give Hunter the bowling. Hunter, settling down to his game, cut the last ball wristily and fine past second slip, and it beat even the energetic Boggs to the boundary.

The Tillingfold players and the crowd, now swollen by the after-tea strollers waiting for the pubs to open at six o'clock, clapped loudly as Bobby called for twenty to go up on the board. Although the sun was still as bright as it had been all day, they felt as though the clouds had been overhead for the past twenty minutes or so.

Bason took a four off the first ball of Mohinder's next over, glancing a full toss to the fine leg boundary and causing Mohinder to signal long leg to move round some twenty yards. The next ball was a short long hop which lifted a bit and Fred, right behind the line, hit it high and hard for four, the ball bouncing once, just where fine leg had been before. Mohinder, furious, unleased his fastest ball, beating Fred completely and shaving the leg bail. Certain that the wicket must have gone, Mohinder did a little dance of agony; and Verrall, thinking he was overdoing the dramatics somewhat, called out, 'You'll 'ave to 'it the stumps if you want to get 'im out.'

Mohinder tried again and again nearly got through. Bason came down at the very last minute to dig out a yorker from his blockhole. The fifth ball Mohinder moved away from the bat off the seam, and Bason, getting a touch, was lucky that the catch did not carry to Agnew at first slip. He went down, and managed only to half-stop the ball on the half-volley, giving away a single.

Frank Hunter failed to get a touch to the last ball, causing Mohinder once again to hold his head in his hands in frustration. Bason strolled down the pitch, prodding at minor irregularities with the toe of his bat. Hunter came to meet him, like two soldiers in a minefield.

'Sorry, Frank. Didn't mean to pinch the bowling.'

'S'all right, Fred. It don't matter who scores, so long as one of us does.'

Although he felt confident of winning with three wickets already under his belt, Troughton realized that the pair were settling down too well. He had a word with Agnew. 'I'm going to pressurize them a bit. Let's call up the troops.'

He brought up Van den Berg to leg slip, added another gully and went forward himself to stand in a menacing position at short extra cover, about ten yards from the bat. Agnew, heartened by this display of strength, bowled his best over yet – a maiden – to Bason, whose bat, whether he was on the front or the back foot, seemed to the bowler to grow ever broader. No runs came, but neither did the bowler look like disturbing Bason's equanimity.

'Well bowled, Alan. Keep it up.'

For Troughton, time at this stage of the game was as important as wickets. If he could restrict the Tillingfold rate of scoring, then they would be under more pressure later to go for a win. He tossed the ball to Mohinder.

'Keep it tight, Ahmed.'

The lithe Pakistani did his best. Three balls fizzed past the bat, missing first the off stump, then the leg and the last going straight but high over the top of the stumps. The fourth ball, savagely short, reared up at Hunter's face, and he was forced to duck hastily out of the way to save his skull. A little buzz ran round the ground.

'That'll get Frank's back up, if nothing else does,' Verrall said to Trine, who'd changed by now and was watching the play with the rest of the team.

Hunter was indeed angry. Mohinder's next ball also rose sharply but this time the batsman stood his ground and swatted fiercely at it. The ball careered off the top edge of ths bat over the wicketkeeper's head and, travelling fast, beat the fielders' chase to the boundary.

'They all count, Frank,' called Fred; and Frank, grinning, waved cheerfully back. He was immersed in the game now, his differences, real or imaginary, with the rest of the world submerged in the twin tasks of scoring runs and keeping his wicket intact. He looked back to check where the wicketkeeper was standing – well back from the wicket. He was pretty sure that after two short balls Mohinder would pitch the next one up, looking for a yorker. So he moved his guard a full foot up the pitch, standing well clear of his crease. If the bowler noticed the move, it might put him off his length anyway; if not, then the intended yorker might well be turned into a full toss. As he had anticipated, it came at him fast and full. Hunter met it with the short sharp jab, right in the meat of the bat, and the ball sped past square leg to the boundary before the fielder could move.

'That was a shot and a half,' said Bobby in admiration, as the spectators broke into genuine applause for a masterly hit. 'Four all the way.'

Chapter 9

Gauvinier glanced round the empty dressing room, which was in its familiar chaos. He liked a moment or two of quiet before an innings, although he knew he must soon go outside to accustom his eyes to the bright light. The first team bag was lying open on the table, its contents scattered all round the room. Clothing, on pegs and half-in, half-out of cricket bags, on the lockers and even on the floor; shoes, boots, bats, pads, gloves and 'boxes' mingled in amiable confusion. Gauvinier was ready; his 'box' comfortable in its 'jock-strap'; his pads not too tight, with the buckles on the inside of the leg, his sleeves rolled up and the bottoms of his trousers tucked neatly into his socks. His batting gloves, personal property which he always refused to lend to anybody, lay beside his bat. They were of an old-fashioned type still fancied by several county cricketers, with 'sausage' fingers and no palm, so that the thumb-piece was connected by wide elastic, which twirled round the wrist twice before fitting on the thumb itself. It leaves the hand in direct contact with the bat handle. Gauvinier would say, 'You can really feel the stroke.'

He picked up his bat. He'd an idea it was going to be needed today, and he wished he was as confident as he'd like to be. It was a 'Warsop', his favourite, and as he stroked it, feeling the silky surface that spoke of long use and careful oiling, he recalled that day, thirty-eight years ago, when he'd been taken to see the old man himself, the great Walter Warsop, one warm spring morning.

His father had driven him in the upright Jowett Eight, rattling and bumping through the winding Essex lanes. They'd turned into a driveway lined with thick clumps of rhododendrons, their flowers blazing purple in the dappled light. At the end of the drive a tall, gabled, redbrick house stood by itself seeming to the young Gauvinier's eyes to grow out of a confusion of tall weeds, flowers and rosebuds. There was dark green moss growing between the stones on the gravel path that led round the left of the house, and there was a level patch of grass that looked as if it had once been a tennis court. Half of it was covered with long mounds of short logs, each cut roughly into the shape of a cricket bat and laid carefully one way and then the other, to allow the air to pass between them. They had all weathered through the winter into a fine shade of grey, almost silver. There must have been thousands, thought Gauvinier, wondering how much memory had exaggerated.

The remainder of the old tennis court was laid out as a cricket net, and there a group of men, some in jackets and others in shirt-sleeves, chatted between themselves. Paul Gauvinier, who was usually a shy man, seemed surprisingly at home in these strangers' company. 'Come along young Peter,' he said. 'Meet Mr Warsop, who's going to make you your first real cricket bat.' Gauvinier remembered a nut-brown, wrinkled face with bright blue eyes and hair the silver-grey of the willow logs, very thin on top.

'So this is the young man,' he had said. 'Come along, then, you must have a knock and we can see what to do about you.' He took Peter by the hand and they went into a long light shed, with windows all down the south side over a cluttered workbench. There were cricket bats in various stages of manufacture, and strange tools – double-handled knives, with the blade at right angles in between the handles; adzes and planes and sandpaper blocks. The floor was strewn with wood shavings and sawdust, and in the bright light a fine golden dust hovered over everything, along with an overpowering smell of linseed oil.

The old man took young Gauvinier to some racks at the back and picked out a bat.

'Try that, young man,' he said. 'That's right, pick it up. No, no, that's too big for you . . . here, try this one.'

Gauvinier hefted the bat in both hands. It felt light and easy – different from the bats he'd used at his prep school or had picked up in the shops. He said so.

'Ah, that's because you've been using bats that are too big for you.' The old man turned to his father. 'I thought you knew better than that, Paul. You should never buy a bat for a youngster that's too big. His muscles aren't made for it, and before you know where you are, he's got all sorts of bad habits.'

They went back to the net, Gauvinier carrying the new bat gingerly.

'Now you may have heard of these gentlemen,' called Walter. 'This small one is Mr Jack O'Connor, and the two big ones are Mr Nicholls and Mr Farnes. And that one there chewing his moustache is Mr Peter Smith. They're going to try to bowl you out. Don't let them.'

So young Gauvinier's first formal coaching session had come from four of the best-known players of the day, three of whom had represented England before and after the war. He grinned at the memory. Much good had it done him; Tillingfold was the height of his achievement and his ambition. But he'd remembered that day, bright and warm within him, as one of the happiest of his life. His new bat had arrived by post four days later. He could still recall its smell.

He was awoken from his reverie by a raucous appeal which had the sound of conviction in it; and he looked through the window to see Bason trudging gloomily back towards the pavilion, swinging his bat at the unoffending daisies and hanging his head.

Gauvinier hurried out into the fresh air, blinking in the bright light. He was disorientated; he had no idea how long he'd been daydreaming and he felt foolish, not knowing what had happened. It was a strange and disconcerting feeling.

He heard the scorer call, 'Forty-seven, four, last man sixteen,' and realized he'd missed at least one over; and also he hadn't had a word with Paul White on his way to the crease.

'Well played, Fred,' he heard his own voice. 'I didn't see what happened. How were you out?'

'Got too confident,' said Bason. 'Me and Frank were going fine and I decided to knock young Agnew off his length. Ball was a bit too far outside the off stump. I took a swing and got a touch. That big black spider behind the sticks doesn't miss chances like that.'

In fact, he and Hunter had set about Agnew to some purpose. He'd driven the young man past extra cover for two runs and then pulled his next ball hard for three. Frank had taken a simple single; and Bason had glanced the next ball very neatly for four. But then he was out. Between the two of them they'd put up a stand for thirty-four, all off the bat. Bason had hit sixteen of them.

Gauvinier looked at his watch. Ten past six. Ninety-two runs left to win, eighty minutes left. It wasn't drastic, yet, but with four wickets down the game was pretty evenly balanced. He saw Hunter have a word with young White as he arrived at the crease, and then he settled down to take the next over from Mohinder.

The Pakistani had had no luck since his first ball, but he'd been bowling well enough and felt he should have had at least a couple more wickets. He regarded Hunter as his natural prey, having already made him snick one over Dewbury's head. But Hunter, with his eye in, was not an easy man to shift. He was particularly severe on anything short of a length and as Mohinder persisted in dropping the ball short, Frank Hunter was in his element.

He hooked the first ball easily for two runs. The next he let go by wide of the leg stump, looking pointedly at the umpire as if to persuade him to signal a wide. The third ball was a rank long hop, which Hunter pulled hard and high for six, the ball dropping just over the boundary, out of reach of Norman Smith's jump at long leg. A ripple of applause ran round the ground for the six and the passing of the fifty mark; the applause swelled as Hunter slashed rather wildly at the next ball and, connecting on the half-volley, sent it swerving over cover point's head for another four.

'Steady, Frank,' murmured Gauvinier to himself. But Hunter had the bit between his teeth now and was advancing up the wicket to Mohinder well before he'd completed his run-up. Mohinder saw him coming and produced the classic counter-attack – a short ball pitched wide outside the off stump. Frank slashed at it and sliced it high in the air, but direct to cover point where Spencer, well underneath the ball, caught it with professional ease.

Hunter retired, well pleased with his knock, to a well-deserved round of applause. Gauvinier rose, picked up his batting gloves, straightened his cap and strode off to the wicket. If ever there was a time for a captain's innings, he thought, it's now. Sixty for five. Seventy-nine runs to win and only an hour and ten minutes in which to get them. Raveley were certainly well on top, in spite of Hunter's hitting.

Gauvinier, determined not to let impetuousness get the better of him, lifted his bat to Mohinder's first ball and watched horrified as it cut back at him off the pitch and narrowly missed the top of the off stump. How many times had his father told him, 'You've been given a bat to hit the ball with. Use it. You're playing cricket, not soldiers, so don't shoulder arms. Anyone who's out not playing a shot deserves to be.' It was ungrammatical, but memorable.

'Pretty close, that,' said Dewbury cheerfully, passing him as he changed ends at the finish of the over. Gauvinier didn't answer. It was one of his little superstitions that he didn't speak to the opposition on the field while he was batting – it was as if he transferred virtue to the enemy. He bent down and carefully slid a stalk of grass out from its tough outer sheath. He liked to moisten his mouth, but could not stand the professional habit of chewing gum. He'd even been known to switch off the television set in the key moments of a vital match because the camera closed in on a batsman chewing away with his mouth wide open.

At the other end, Paul White, fully aware of the crisis, faced Agnew's over with a great deal of confidence. Although he'd left school a couple of years ago, and had drifted around from job to job since, he had played alongside and against Agnew in school teams for years and knew himself to be fully able to cope with him. Gauvinier often felt that White epitomized what for his generation might well be known as the exasperating seventies. The young man was highly intelligent, confident in himself and his opinions, never frightened to criticize the older generation for everything from the atom bomb to the standard of television advertisements. He'd sailed into grammar school at the age of eleven, but (deliberately, his parents and masters felt) had failed his O-level examinations and left school at sixteen. Since then he'd drifted from job to job, and for the past three months had been a meter-reader for the local electricity board, regaling his drinking partners in the public bar of 'The Dog and Duck' with scandalous and highly spiced accounts of his exploits with the younger housewives on the new estate. He was a great fan of Chelsea Football Club, and on Saturdays in the winter was a familiar, loud-mouthed figure on trains into Victoria, several times narrowly escaping the attentions of the law.

To Gauvinier, the fact that White played cricket at all was a redeeming feature, but even here he seemed destined to provide his elders with more disappointment. He had remarkable natural talent, and was quite capable of coming up with a dazzling performance such as the catch with which he'd dismissed Spencer in the first innings. But when he'd been picked to go to the county nets in the winter, he'd gone along once, watched one session of coaching in (for him) comparative silence, and refused to go again. When asked the reason he replied, 'Too bloody dull. I don't like messing about with lads.' Now he waited for Agnew's first ball, casually tapping his bat in the crease, and then with all the time in the world steered it away to third man for an easy two runs. The next one cut back at him and he played back, a fraction too casually, the ball nicking off the bat and hitting him with a hollow thud in the 'box'. He dropped his bat, staggered back, and doubled over clutching himself with both hands.

'Eeeh,' chuckled Verrall, not without sympathy and from the safety of his deck chair. 'That'll do his marriage prospects not a lot of good.'

Agnew and the fielders clustered round the doubled-up figure, rubbing White's stomach but really performing the more useful function of hiding his embarrassment as well as his agony from the curious view of the public. Every batsman knows that 'one in the box' is genuine agony; and that agony lasts – in all but the most serious cases, when the unfortunate victim has forgotten to wear his protector – maybe a minute or two. In that time all he can do is to moan, and groan, and blow through his teeth while waiting for the pain to pass; and hope at the same time he's not making too much of a spectacle of himself.

Eventually, amid sympathetic applause, White recovered his composure, his bat and his batting gloves, and was ready to take strike again. Far from being scared by this experience, as he might have been, he was in fact furiously angry. To the astonishment of the bowler, he hit the next three balls for four – two drives and a square cut, and ended the over by walking down the wicket and thrashing the ball straight back over Agnew's head for a straight six into the chestnut trees. The field rang with applause, and Gauvinier, applauded too by clapping one gloved hand against his bat, went up the pitch to deliver the obligatory warning about not being too rash. But he checked himself when he saw the young man's white face and furious eyes.

'Well hit, son,' was all he said; and White, still angry, answered fiercely, 'No bugger's going ter hit me in the balls and get away with it.'

The burst of hitting had sent the pendulum of the match, always moving from one side to the other, swinging firmly in Tillingfold's favour, at least for the moment. Now the total was eighty: it wasn't yet half past six, and for the first time Tillingfold were up with the clock and the run rate necessary to win.

Gauvinier, always suspicious when things were going well, was content to play himself in during Mohinder's next over, taking a two with a little tucked-in shot to mid-wicket and otherwise getting the feel of the pitch as best he could. But he was relieved to feel that the pressure was now on the opposite number, Troughton, to win back the initiative.

Troughton was indeed in a quandary. Quite simply, he had no recognized bowlers left. The removal of Graves to hospital meant that he had had to use Mohinder as his 'stock' bowler. When the team had been chosen, the selectors had been satisfied that Tillingfold, a mere village, could easily be contained by three seam bowlers. In normal circumstances, Agnew and Mohinder should have been sufficient to cope with the Tillingfold batting; but few bowlers in this class of cricket could be expected to recover immediately from a thrashing such as had just been administered to Agnew.

Troughton cast around his team in his mind. Brewster, he knew, could turn his arm over a little, but was inclined to be erratic. Van den Berg, the earnest South African, bowled angular off-breaks in the nets, but the last time he'd tried him in a match he'd failed to get one to pitch on the wicket. Raveley couldn't afford another over like Agnew's last one. And Dewbury – Dewbury was keeping wicket.

Troughton called Spencer over to ask him if he'd mind putting the pads on and keeping wicket, to release Dewbury for an over or two. Spencer, willing as ever, didn't mind a bit, and play was held up for another couple of minutes while Spencer donned the wicketkeeper's pads and the complicated arrangement of straps and buckles that made up the wicketkeeper's protective equipment. Then he put on the undergloves, made of fine kid, moist and sticky with sweat; and finally the big heavily padded gloves with knobbly rubber fingers. Spencer flexed his hands a couple of times, the stiff gloves inhibiting his movements, but enjoying the strange feeling of the new challenge. He had, in fact, kept wicket a few times before, when nobody else had wanted to, and was cricketer enough to know that he could perform quite well, so long as nobody expected him to come up with a snappy leg-side stumping.

The delay irked Gauvinier, because it used up valuable time; and the break allowed Paul White to sample the after-effects of the blow he had received. His groin was sore and he felt sick. But eventually the change was made and the lanky Dewbury prepared to bowl.

Perhaps it was because his hands, accustomed to their gloves, were still stiff; or maybe it was because Dewbury had not bowled in a match for some time. Whatever the reason, his first ball seemed to stick in his palm and it hit the ground about two yards in front of him, bouncing slowly down the wicket towards the batsman.

White, scarcely able to believe his eyes and his luck, watched the ball bounce a third time. Then hit it with all his force, intending to lift it straight over the bowler's head for another six. Dewbury, watching the dreadful ball bounce slowly down the wicket, resigned himself to anything the batsman cared to do, and to his astonishment and delight it flew like a bullet straight at him. He caught the full-blooded drive two-handed at his shoulder. It was probably the worst ball he'd ever bowled in his life.

It took the rest of the team a second or two to appreciate that a wicket had fallen. They had been looking towards the boundary where the ball should have gone. But then they crowded round the big Jamaican, slapping him on the back and laughing. Gauvinier was appalled. The luck had turned again, with a vengeance.

At that moment there was not one man on the ground who gave Tillingfold a chance of drawing the game, much less of winning it. Gauvinier resigned himself to playing for an honourable draw, although with an hour's batting left and only four wickets to fall he knew Tillingfold would need all the luck they could find to last out. Still, the score, eighty-two, six, twenty, went up on the board, and the field applauded White for his defiant hitting all the way to the pavilion. Joe Deacon marched jauntily to the crease and Gauvinier felt that all was not lost yet.

'Don't worry, guv, we can do it,' Deacon said as he passed Gauvinier on his way to the crease. 'You stop 'em. I'll hit 'em.'

'You just concentrate on staying there, young Joe,' said Gauvinier, pleased by the show of spirit. 'None of your tip and run, now.'

Joe Deacon was not, in fact, a hitter. But he liked to imagine himself as a second Alan Knott, and indeed had scored a great many runs in the time by prodding and glancing, and running for everything. He crouched almost behind the bat at the crease, moving his feet restlessly, and his back-lift went out towards point. But he brought the bat down quickly and nearly always in line with the ball; and he was a good partner to have at the other end.

He parried his first two balls from Dewbury, who after his first lucky lapse settled down to bowl steadily at around medium pace. To the third Deacon moved rapidly across his stumps and, as Dewbury was opening his mouth to appeal for lbw, flicked the ball at the last minute past square leg. He had time to grin cockily at Dewbury as he turned to saunter back for the second run. The next ball he half stopped, half pushed off his legs, again a yard or two to leg, and Gauvinier, backing up fast, called for, and got, a quick single. Gauvinier, feeling his spirits rise, hit the next ball, a half-valley, uppishly but safely to mid-wicket for another single, which turned into three as Spencer, unused to his clumsy pads and gloves, missed the hard return which came in from Brewster. Boggs, backing up, had a long way to run for the ball.

Tillingfold had lost a wicket, but had scored six runs in the last over. Leaning on his bat after the exertion of running the three, Gauvinier was sufficiently encouraged to make some calculations. Six runs since the last wicket – that made eighty-eight. Fifty runs behind. Fifty-one to win in – Gauvinier looked at the church clock – fifty minutes. But only four wickets left.

All round the ground players and spectators were making similar calculations. Assuming no wickets fell, Tillingfold should make the runs easily. But that was too great an assumption. Say, then, that a wicket or two were to fall and that Raveley managed to bowl ten more overs in the time. Tillingfold had to score at five runs an over to win. 'Sounds easy, said like that,' Bason commented to Hunter.

Easy. Gauvinier had 'farmed' the bowling and now faced Mohinder. The tall Pakistani, taking his time over each ball, forced him on to the defensive, and he had to concede a maiden over. Once more the applause rippled round the ground as the spectators, sensing the atmosphere, settled in their seats to enjoy a close finish.

The field changed over slowly at the end of the over. Troughton and Dewbury spent what seemed to the batsmen an inordinate time in making minute adjustments to the field. Their sentiments were shared by a number of the spectators and Trine, thoroughly disgusted with such delaying tactics, called 'Get on with it', in a voice which echoed round the field. There was a ripple of laughter, and the church clock began chiming the three-quarters past the hour. The youngsters took up the chant, as they'd done over the years, to the tune of the bells.

'Play up Tillingfold. Play up Tillingfold. Play up Tillingfold.' The rhythmic melody never failed to hearten Gauvinier, who considered it the village's answer to the dreary, meaningless songs of soccer supporters. 'We shall not, we shall not be moved . . . Just like the tree that's standing by the waterside . . .' Gauvinier, who'd marched from Aldermaston to Hyde Park in the cause of peace, felt moved to violence every time he watched 'Match of the Day'.

Gauvinier filled the time by doing something he should have done twenty minutes or so before. He called for Albert Jess to come on to the field and take the place of Norman Smith, who could be needed to bat shortly. Jess trotted out to the square leg position, and Smith went in to pad up.

Troughton, having turned the psychological screw another fraction, went back to his place at mid-off, and Dewbury put down a fast long hop dead on the middle stump to Deacon. The little wicketkeeper, using his fast footwork, was across his wicket in a flash and dabbing, rather than hooking the ball down to square leg for a single. Jess, competent and keen not to appear slacking when he was fielding for the other side, leapt after the ball smartly, stopping any chance of a second run.

'Here then,' Fred Bason called indignantly, 'you don't have to run them out, you know.'

Gauvinier drove the next ball hard to cover point, but sent the eager Deacon, who was backing up too hastily, back to his crease. He blocked the next two balls and then, losing his patience, swung clean across a ball which came in to him and keeping rather low, narrowly missed the leg stump. Spencer failed to get his body behind the ball and it skidded past his pads for a bye.

'Ninety up,' called Bobby, and had to repeat it because his

voice was lost in the clapping. By now even a bye merited applause if you were on Tillingfold's side.

Deacon half cut, half swatted the last ball of the over into the gully; but the batsmen mutually agreed not to run, in order to leave Gauvinier with the bowling.

'Run up' came the cry from the pavilion, where the Tillingfold players were anxious not to see any possible run lost. 'Could have got two there,' grumbled Trine, forgetting how he'd run himself out.

Forty minutes left; forty-eight runs to tie, forty-nine to win. The time factor was beginning to turn against Tillingfold. But it wasn't yet crucial, if Gauvinier could get his strokes moving. Mohinder, whipping the ball down still at a smart pace, gave him little opportunity to score. He pitched the ball fractionally short of a length, bringing it into the batsman and forcing him on to the back foot. With six men on the leg side and three on the off, there was precious little opportunity for Gauvinier to score. He played four balls carefully down on the leg side to one or the other of the short legs, knowing that he must not allow his impatience to get the better of him. It was a case of who would crack first, the bowler or the batsman.

'I bet the guv's steaming out there,' Fred Bason commented to Frank Hunter. 'He likes to have a go.'

Gauvinier, as Spencer had done in the Raveley innings, cautiously moved his guard a foot or so down the pitch. He was not out to hit, but merely to turn the short ball into one of drivable length. Mohinder saw the move, and tried to tempt him into a mistake with a slower ball, which Gauvinier saw in time and patted, on the half-volley, gravely back down the pitch.

Now every ball began to take on a significance of its own. Mohinder bowled again, Gauvinier, forward defensively, missed, and was rapped hard on the front pad. Mohinder appealed, vehemently. Umpire Fanshawe remained motionless, expressionless. Gauvinier stayed confidently where he was a second or two to indicate to the whole field, as well as to himself, how impossible the appeal was.

But if he'd hoped to rattle the bowler into producing a loose ball, his effort was mistimed. Fanshawe called 'Over', and marched off to square leg. There was another round of applause for Mohinder's second maiden over.

Now the position was beginning to look difficult for Tillingfold. One run had been scored in the last three overs; the time was five minutes to seven, and forty-nine were still needed to win.

The first ball of Dewbury's next over rapped Deacon on the pads and rebounded a couple of yards back up the pitch. 'Come on,' shouted Gauvinier, hurling himself down the wicket. The pitch seemed to erupt, as Dewbury went for the ball. Deacon ran as if the hounds of hell were on his tail. Dewbury, to save time, kicked soccer style at the wicket as Gauvinier, despairing of making his ground, dived headlong with his bat outstretched. He would have been out had Dewbury's kick succeeded; but the ball missed the wicket by an inch and Spencer, scrambling up towards the stumps, could not retrieve it in time.

Gauvinier dusted himself down, getting his breath back as the applause died. Dewbury ran up to bowl again. One pace, two, three, four, five, six and over went his arm. Gauvinier, sensing at the last moment that the ball was going to swing away from him, dropped his wrists and checked his stroke, allowing the bat to follow the swing of the ball and turning a full-blooded off-drive into a directed push wide of gully and down towards third man. As he ran an easy two, Gauvinier could feel the pleasure surge thrugh him, and with it came confidence. He had played the stroke exactly as he meant it, feeling it go in the precise direction he'd intended, off the meat of the bat, and with the timing that only instinct can give. He knew in his bones that Tillingfold could get the runs.

Dewbury's next ball was not a bad one – slightly short, just outside the off stump. Gauvinier, full of new-found confidence, put his left foot down the wicket and, 'on the up', thrashed the ball contemptuously away to the cover boundary. Brewster, in the covers, dived gallantly in an effort to stop the four, but the ball was past him while he was still in mid-air. The Tillingfold players cheered as one man; even the Raveley players stood applauding the shot.

Hands on hips, Dewbury grinned at Gauvinier. 'Say, man,

that one came from Viv Richards,' he said without rancour. 'Bit of luck,' Gauvinier answered, knowing in his heart while he said it that you could not play a shot like that unless you really did have cricket in your marrow. But the match wasn't done yet. The ball was retrieved and tossed back on to the field by one of the Tillingfold youngsters. Brewster went to pick it up, but he was beaten to it by a large black mongrel, which had appeared from nowhere.

Brewster, who had a healthy respect for strange dogs, approached cautiously. 'Here boy, down boy, put it down.' He advanced slowly with one hand out, as if he were offering a biscuit. 'Here, boy. Here, old chap.' The dog allowed him to approach and then bounded off across the field, leaving Brewster stranded in his wake. 'Guess he just doesn't like biscuits,' he muttered.

Jess, the substitute, tried to head the dog off, arms outstretched. The dog veered sharply towards the centre of the field where three or four players endeavoured to corner it. The dog stopped, put the ball down and stood over it, panting. Troughton, slowly, so as not to alarm the animal, ventured closer and closer, and jumped back in alarm as the dog barked sharply, twice.

By this time the field was in uproar, spectators shouting advice and laughing in equal quantities. Gauvinier leaned on his bat, deliberately avoiding becoming involved in order to keep himself calm; his mind on the time. Three fielders made abortive efforts to collar either the ball or the dog; but each time they tried the animal seized the ball in its teeth again and ran off a few yards, enjoying the romp. Eventually, they headed it towards the pavilion, where Bill Budgeon, limping forward said quietly, 'Bring it here, boy,' and fondling the animal gently behind its ears, tossed the ball back to the nearest fielder. He had something of a similar effect on very small children.

But three minutes had been lost; and by the time Gauvinier had played out the rest of the over, defensively, so as to regain his concentration, the clock had struck seven. The scoreboard read: ninety-seven, six, twenty.

Chapter 10

With only half an hour left and forty-one runs to make against a tight bowling attack, Gauvinier and Deacon felt the pressure building up against them. It was not ones and twos that they needed now, but fours and sixes; and these seemed very hard to come by. Deacon felt keenly that he should be giving the bowling to Gauvinier at every opportunity. He himself was not a maker of fours and he had never hit a six in his life. But Troughton was also well aware of this and for the first four balls of each over that Deacon faced he set the field so as to prevent any chance of a single.

He put four fielders on a line some fifteen yards from the bat on both the off and the leg sides; it was like a Sunday League professional field setting, aimed at preventing runs rather than at taking wickets. The only fielder outside the pattern was out on the boundary at deep mid-wicket, and this was the substitute, Jess. His is always the most invidious task in cricket. In the first-class game his job is somewhat different – the twelfth man helps with the team's baggage, brings on the drinks at regular intervals, scores in emergencies and fields as substitute if one of his team is off the field. It is a not very onerous, rather frustrating task, given usually to the newly joined recruit. His name will not be mentioned in the scorebook; even a brilliant catch is entered as 'caught sub'. But at least the twelfth man is working for his own side. In village cricket, the substitute is usually a reasonably keen member of the opposing side acting as a deputy, and his temporary function is to get his own side out. If he drops a catch, misses a run-out, or gently helps a ball over the boundary with his boot, he is branded in all eyes as a bad sportsman. If he fields brilliantly, throws down the wicket or saves a series of fours, he is bound to be castigated. 'You needn't have tried that hard . . .' He cannot win.

But Albert Jess was one of those fortunate individuals who did not really care which side he was on, so long as he was playing cricket. He would probably have preferred to catch out a member of the other side rather than one of his own. But when he was on the field he forgot which side he was playing for and did everything to the best of his (quite reasonable) ability.

So when Deacon in desperation lofted Mohinder's first ball over the inner ring of fielders some ten yards to Jess's left, he ran into position for the catch without a second thought. But he lost the ball in the sun, which was by now halfway down towards the roof of the pavilion, and, blinded, allowed it to drop almost vertically a foot in front of his cupped hands. He seized the ball on the bounce, and flung it back to the wicket-keeper furiously, calling out 'Sorry, skipper' to Troughton as he did so. Troughton, manfully concealing his chagrin, knew what Jess was feeling and replied, 'I know, it's the devil at this time of day.' But they both knew how the dropped catch appeared and neither was comforted by Frank Hunter's cheerful bellow from the pavilion, 'Well played, our side.' Jess went miserably back to his place, wondering if it had really been necessary for him to look at the sun. He was determined not to be found wanting again, and was glad for a hard chase to cut off Gauvinier's shot off the next ball, glanced off a full toss round wide of Jess's right hand. Jess, running hard, stretched out his foot at the last moment and stopped the ball before it crossed the boundary, overrunning and having to scamper back to pick it up and throw in while the batsmen took two runs.

The burst of applause for a sporting piece of fielding swelled round the field as the one hundred went up on the scoreboard. It was as though players and spectators alike realized that a significant landmark had been passed.

'That's better, but we're not out of the wood yet,' Fred Bason pondered out loud. And Colin Verrall, waiting to bat next in a ferment of excitement showed his tension by the break in his voice as he replied, 'Nothing to worry about. He's been saving me for this one. Oh gor blimey, look at them two!'

Gauvinier had hit the third ball from Mohinder round to leg. Agnew, fielding a few yards from square leg, flung himself to his right, half stopped the ball, and with extraordinary speed leapt after it and flung it hard and low at Gauvinier's wicket.

Deacon backing up in the approved style and alert for any runs going, called 'wait' as the shot left the bat. Then, as the ball rolled away from Agnew's hand, he called 'come on'; and then frantically as he saw Agnew seize the ball, 'Get back. Get back.'

Gauvinier, who'd hesitated, moved, and turned back, like a puppet on a string, once more dived in desperation to reach the crease. Flat on his stomach, with his bat along the ground, he saw the ball hit the wicket well after he was home and ricochet past him up the pitch, catching Deacon unprepared as he sauntered back towards the bowler. By some extraordinary chance the ball rebounded straight up the wicket to hit the stumps at the other end – with Deacon well out of his crease.

The Raveley fielders, who had appealed as one man for the run-out at Gauvinier's end, instantly appealed again. The two 'Howzats!' came within a couple of seconds of each other, leaving every spectator, and the fielders themselves, throughly confused.

'Not out,' said the Raveley umpire at Gauvinier's end.

'Out,' said Oliver Fanshawe, raising his finger to Deacon.

Deacon, dismayed, opened his mouth to protest, but Fanshawe shook his head at him.

'You were out of your crease, so you were run out.'

'Yes, but the ball had broke the wicket at the other end.' Deacon was determined to have his say.

'Indeed. But as the other batsman was given not out, the ball was not yet dead. Had it run on for four overthrows, you'd have taken that.'

'I suppose so.' And Deacon dragged himself unwillingly off the pitch to the pavilion, where he received much sympathy and praise for a brave and perky innings. But he refused to be consoled, and stormed off grumpily to change into his 'civvies', as he called them.

The score went up on the board: one hundred, seven, five.

Colin Verrall arrived at the wicket, with the news that Colonel Trine and the nurses had returned to the ground having left young Graves in Billington hospital with suspected appendicitis. His mother and father had been located and they were even now on their way to the hospital.

Gauvinier, who was anxious to get on with the game, shooed Verrall to the bowler's end and waited impatiently for Mohinder's next ball. As it swung into his body Gauvinier went down on his right knee and swinging across the line of the ball, picked it up and hit it high over the fine leg boundary for six. The Tillingfold applause was as if for a reprieve from death.

Mohinder swore a Pakistani oath under his breath and delivered a beautiful ball, moving slightly off the seam from middle to off stump, and Gauvinier, caught in mid-stroke, played a little jab at it and was very lucky not to touch the ball to Spencer, standing comfortably back for the catch. Thinking only of keeping his wicket intact, he patted the next ball, a simple half-volley, back to the bowler; then realizing what he'd missed, he slapped his bat angrily against his pads, hurting his leg.

'Play up, Tillingfold.' The youngsters took up their chant once more, and Gauvinier realized with something of a jolt that it was still only six minutes past seven, and that at one hundred and six for seven, the game was still very much in the balance.

The new batsman, Verrall, had few pretensions. He liked what he called a good hit and no nonsense. 'A short life and a merry one,' was his motto. Gauvinier walked up the wicket in the vain hope that Verrall would heed some friendly advice. 'Don't try to hit the cover off the ball first thing, Colin,' he cautioned. 'We can win this if we go steady.'

'Leave it to me, guv.' Colin grinned. He had his own recipe for crisis: 'Knock 'em off their length.'

But to show that he had heeded his captain's advice he played forward cautiously to Dewbury's first ball and patted it away on the off side. He took a couple of paces up the wicket to tease Gauvinier, who wouldn't be drawn, and tempted Brewster at cover point to try to throw the wicket down. Brewster feinted a quick throw, sending Verrall back hurriedly, and then tossed the ball slowly back to the bowler.

The next ball Verrall pulled round from outside the off stump, high in the air. It was a repeat of the previous over's chance for Jess; but this time the substitute, moving under the ball and keeping the sun to his left, judged the catch nicely and was pleased to hold it. Verrall, the smile wiped off his face for a moment or two, jogged off on his way to the pavilion, watching the little 'duck' appear on the bottom line of the scoreboard. One hundred and six, eight, nought. Gauvinier's optimism, along with that of much of the Tillingfold team, was a fragile thing.

But there was still room for hope, if not optimism. The batsmen, going for the run in case Jess had dropped the catch, had crossed; and Gauvinier, with his eye well set, was facing the bowling. Norman Smith, the new man in at the other end, was the same type of batsman as Verrall, but he was young and fresh enough to be more inclined to follow his captain's instructions.

Troughton had a word with the bowler, and spread his field wider to tempt Gauvinier into taking a single. But Gauvinier, anticipating the short ball coming in to his body, was across like a flash, and rolling his wrists over, achieved a classic hook, the ball hit down towards the ground rather than up, and it went scorching past square leg, forcing the umpire to jump out of the way. Four runs.

'Hundred and ten up.'

'Don't worry, youngster, we'll do the sums now.' Trine had taken over charge of the scoreboard and was marking every run scored.

'Play up, Tillingfold.' The men now added their chant to the boys', hushing themselves as Dewbury ran in to deliver the next ball. Gauvinier drove at it, flicked it high in the air through the empty space where second slip might have been, and managed another two. The next was the last ball of the over, and Gauvinier was already moving as he played the ball gently forward. Smith was off like a flash from the other end, and they made the run before any fielders could get near the ball.

'Easy, Tillingfold, easy.'

'Well run, sir. It's amazing what you can do if you try.'

'Easy, easy, easy, easy.'

Once more the church clock struck. Seven-fifteen. Twenty-six to win.

'Keep it up, boy,' Gauvinier said quietly to Norman. 'We need about eight an over. Let me have the bowling if you can. If you find yourself facing, stop anything that's straight and hit anything that's off the wicket. But don't let's run each other out.'

Smith grinned at him. 'It's a hell of a finish, sir, isn't it?'

'Will be, if we're lucky.'

Now Troughton brought back Agnew for a last fling, calculating that the young man would have recovered from the thrashing he'd received earlier, and might well blast his way through to a wicket. Gauvinier played his first ball away firmly on the off side, but sent Smith back when the youngster tried to run.

'Run up, Tillingfold,' came the inevitable cry from the pavilion.

Agnew, walking slowly back to his mark and polishing the ball on his trousers, reckoned that a yorker might surprise Gauvinier. But a man who is set will quite often treat a yorker as a full toss; and Gauvinier, moving forward smoothly, met the ball with the full face of the bat, not bothering to run as he watched it scorch straight back past the bowler to the sight-screen. Four more runs.

Now, he thought to himself, with a certainty that owed nothing to reason, that young man is going to bowl a short ball outside the off stump. And his clairvoyance enabled him to be across the wicket in position to pull when it came very hard from off to leg, out past mid-on for another four.

'On target,' he muttered to himself.

Troughton said quietly as Agnew walked back towards him, 'Don't worry about pace. Just get the length right and try to keep him there.' And Agnew, straining every nerve and sinew, produced three lovely balls which Gauvinier had to be content to block.

Ten minutes left now, and as the tension mounted the crowd was reinforced by the early drinkers from 'The Dog and Duck', walking across the road with pints of beer in their hands to lean on the wooden rail under the chestnut trees.

'Keep steady, Norman,' Gauvinier cautioned. 'We can do it. Two more overs, perhaps three if we're lucky.' Provided the umpires were in position before the clock registered the half-hour another over could be bowled.

Troughton took Dewbury off and, sportingly, did not waste time by asking him to change places again with Spencer behind the stumps. He threw the ball to Mohinder. 'Come on, Ghengis Khan,' he said, 'let's see what you're made of.'

Mohinder obliged. His first ball, whipping through and leaping off the pitch towards Smith's chin, had the young man fending it away from his face. It flicked off his glove and straight into Spencer's. Norman, his head down, thumping his bat as he walked, trailed off to the pavilion having achieved the second duck of the innings, his frustration showing in his every move.

'One-twenty-one, nine, nought,' called out Bobby.

'OK,' said Trine. 'I can add nought to nought.'

Budgeon, the least line of resistance (or the last hope, whichever side you happened to be on), shuffled out to the wicket. In spite of his handicap, he steadfastly refused to employ a runner; and indeed had surprising pace in an emergency. But he was hardly the man to take quick singles in a last-minute race for a win. He acknowledged this cheerfully, 'Don't worry, guv. We'll get them in fours.'

Eleven balls to go: eighteen runs to win.

Budgeon took guard, tapped his block quickly, glanced round the field, and was ready.

The first ball was short and fast, outside the off stump. Budgeon hit it stiff-armed out on the off side, square of the wicket and to Brewster's left at cover. Taking the fielders by surprise he bellowed for a quick single to give Gauvinier the bowling. They scrambled home amid cheers from the boundary.

'Go it, Hopalong.' 'Play up, Tillingfold.' 'Let's have another one.'

The second was pitched right up to Gauvinier's toes. Leaning forward, he flicked it round the corner, wide of fine leg, for four runs. Excited applause. Nine balls left now, and thirteen runs wanted.

Gauvinier, taking a chance, walked down the wicket and lifted the next ball high and straight back past the bowler over the sightscreen. There was a crash of tinkling glass, drowned by the shouts from the pavilion, laughter amd more applause. 'Someone's car window,' assumed Gauvinier automatically, without registering the thought, his mind on mathematics, and how to get to the other end to poach the bowling from Budgeon. He didn't want to risk trying for another six. But for the first time Tillingfold were ahead of the equation: one hundred and thirty-two – seven runs to win, and eight balls in which to get them.

Mohinder bowled, and Gauvinier advanced up the pitch again, intending to place it for a single. He missed, the ball rapping him on the pads and shooting away to leg. One leg-bye.

The score was one hundred and thirty-three now. A six would do it, with seven balls to spare. And Budgeon, like a rock, blocked Mohinder's last ball. No runs.

Now there was only the last over left: six balls, with six runs to make and Gauvinier to face. In the scorebox, Bobby Bewers, intent on the game, didn't understand when his fellow-scorer commented, 'A double six', and Groat had to explain: 'Your skipper's on forty-four. He needs a six and Tillingfold need a six.'

The first ball of the last over saw Agnew bowling off his thirty-yard run, to Gauvinier. It was of good length, on the off stump. Gauvinier, controlling his nerves, played it straight back to the bowler's left hand. Agnew, in his keenness, grabbed too soon, and Gauvinier, hesitating at first, called Budgeon to come for the single. Troughton, nipping across smartly from mid-on, picked up cleanly with one hand and should have run Budgeon out by a yard. Instead he shied at the bowler's wicket, missing by a yard and giving the batsmen an easy second run. The tension was alive in the air; and there was hardly any clapping.

Five balls to go. Four runs to win.

The second produced a nice square drive, which should have been the winning shot, except that Dewbury, now fielding at gully, dived to his right and brought off a fine save, two handed. No runs. Still four to win.

'By jingo, what a game!' Trine said under his breath.

The third ball was short, lifting, and Gauvinier hooked, fractionally late. The ball looped from the slice of the bat just over the clutching fingers of leg slip and flew towards the fine leg boundary. Jess, racing after it, brought off another good stop; but even at Budgeon's halting pace, there had been time for the batsmen to take two runs.

Three balls to go. Two runs to make. The calmest man on the field was now Gauvinier. Although conscious of the score, and aware that they had reached the climax of the game, he had no uncertainty left.

He faced Agnew again, lifting his bat and patting it down again gently in time to the bowler's run-up. Once more came the short ball outside the off stump and once more Gauvinier hit his favourite shot, left leg forward, smashing the ball through the cover field, a four from the moment it left the bat.

The match was won by a wicket, with two balls to spare.

Chapter 11

Gauvinier became conscious of applause, of Philip Troughton coming up to him, hand outstretched.

'Well done, Peter, well batted. I thought we'd got you on the run half an hour ago.'

He was walking with Bill Budgeon back to the pavilion, the Raveley players making way for them, and then Budgeon in turn standing back and pushing him forward, to more confused congratulations and slaps on the back. 'Well done, skipper.' 'Great innings, captain.' 'Well done, sir.'

Bobby Bewers thrust himself wriggling through the throng, waving his scorebook. 'I knew you'd do it, sir . . . look! You got your fifty.'

Gauvinier was astonished. His own score was the last thing that he'd been worrying about, but he didn't want to let the boy down, so he grinned and thanked him

The dressing room was filled with people, changing out of flannels, half dressed, chatting. Gauvinier, suddenly exhausted, slumped back on the locker, listening to the babel. Mitterman thrust through the throng.

'Sorry Peter, but can I have 50p please?'

Gauvinier looked blank.

'You owe twenty-five pence for tea and twenty-five more for the kitty.'

There was a cry of protest.

'No, he shouldn't pay into the kitty today. He's won the bloody match for us.' Gauvinier stilled the protest by finding fifty pence in his trouser pocket and handing it over.

'Drinks on me tonight,' he said over the hubbub. 'Beating Raveley's always worth a celebration, to say nothing of a fifty. Pass the word around. "The Dog and Duck" in half an hour.'

It was tradition at Tillingfold that after a match there was a glass for every man on both sides, the umpires and the scorers. The home side forked out the money, and two great jugs of mild and bitter would be carried over from 'The Dog and Duck' to the pavilion, with the glasses, on two trays.

Phil Troughton poked his head round the dressing-room door.

'Skipper, will you all join us in a glass of champagne?'

More uproar and laughter.

'What's this, then? Raveley lashing out?'

'Tillingfold beer not good enough for the likes of you?'

'Somebody's birthday?'

Troughton explained. 'We'd brought the champers in case we won – it would have been our half-century. But you pipped us at the post and now it's forty-nine apiece. It's not worth keeping another year, so let's drink to the next time. In any case, an innings like yours is well worth a drop of champagne.'

'Ay, and a match like that,' said Bason soberly. 'You couldn't have wished for a better finish, anywhere.'

'Thanks a lot, Phil. Tell your lads there's a drink going in "The Dog and Duck" when you've changed.'

The champagne was drunk, and the beer. People collected their kit and their cricket bags and drifted off towards the pub, or to their wives, their children or their girl friends. Colonel Trine put his head around the door and then disappeared after a gruff, 'Well done, Peter. Marvellous knock. Wish I'd seen more of it. Goodnight to you.'

One by one they left, footsteps echoing on the wooden floor, until Gauvinier was alone in the changing-room. He packed his pads into his cricket bag and looked around as he always did to see if anyone had left anything valuable behind. All he could see was an old pair of cricket boots and one (one?) shoe.

He shut the dressing-room door, and locked it; checked round the big centre room that all the windows were closed and let himself out of the pavilion door.

Oliver Fanshawe was sitting on a bench, waiting for him as usual. Without a word, they locked the door of the pavilion and walked companionably along the boundary line under the chestnut trees. The shadows were lengthening now, halfway across the green grass to the wicket; and under the trees it was rich and quiet. Even the swings in the far corner were still.

'That was a very good game, Peter.'

They had paused, by mutual consent. Gauvinier put down his cricket bag. They looked around the silent ground.

'Yes ... yes, it was.' He picked up his bag and swung it round with sudden energy.

'Come on. I'm going to buy the chaps a drink.'

More About Penguins and Pelicans

Penguinews, which appears every month, contains details of all the new books issued by Penguins as they are published. From time to time it is supplemented by *Penguins in Print*, which is our complete list of almost 5,000 titles.

A specimen copy of *Penguinews* will be sent to you free on request. Please write to Dept EP, Penguin Books Ltd, Harmondsworth, Middlesex, for your copy.

In the U.S.A.: For a complete list of books available from Penguins in the United States write to Dept CS, Penguin Books, 625 Madison Avenue, New York, New York 10022.

In Canada: For a complete list of books available from Penguins in Canada write to Penguin Books Canada Ltd, 2801 John Street, Markham, Ontario L3R 1B4.